MW00606895

Collecting Cigarette Lighters Volume II

A Price Guide

By
Neil S. Wood

Layout and Design by
Amy Van Hoosier

L-W Book Sales
& Publishing

Pricing Note

The current values in this book should be used only as a guide. They are not intended to set prices, which vary from one section of the country to another. Auction prices as well as dealer prices vary greatly and are affected by condition as well as demand. Neither the author nor the publisher assumes responsibility for any losses that might be incurred as a result of consulting this guide.

Additional copies of this book may be ordered from:
L-W Book Sales
P.O. Box 69
Gas City, IN 46933

$24.95
Add $2.00 for shipping.

Many other antique & collectible reference books available call 317-674-6450 for a complete catalog.

© Copyright L-W Book Sales, 1995
1st Printing
ISBN# 0-89538-071-4
This book or any part thereof may not be reproduced without written consent of the Author and Publisher.

INTRODUCTION

Thank you for your support of the very successful *Collecting Cigarette Lighters Vol. I* and welcome to the second volume. My first price guide on the subject of cigarette lighters received such an overwhelming response, I realized that this much interest would soon help me generate *Collecting Cigarette Lighters Vol. II*.

Collecting Cigarette Lighters Vol. II is just as useful to the new or experienced collector of lighter memorabilia as is the first book, yet this particular volume contains more of a selection of rare items. Also, many newer Zippo lighters are included to reflect the growing interest in Zippo collecting.

Other collectible trends that are gaining momentum in the lighter field are war-era (especially WWII and Vietnam War) lighters. BEWARE of altered lighters, mostly Zippos from the Vietnamese era. Advertising items and lighter fluid containers are also included prominently in these pages due to increasing prices in the current market.

Welcome to the realm of cigarette lighter collecting, and to those of you that are seasoned veterans of the subject- thanks for helping light the way!!

ACKNOWLEDGMENTS

We owe a great thanks to the many individuals who helped make this book project a reality- and an extra-special thanks goes out to the following people, who in particular were exceptionally invaluable:

Renee Martin
Wes & Elaine Hart
Wayne Stoops
Joyce Layton
Allen Evans
Mert Kallner

BUYING LIGHTERS

Touch Tips - Strikers - Caps
Alcohol Burning - Store Countertops
The Old & Unusual !!!

**RENEE MARTIN
P.O. Box 44090
Columbus, OH 43204
Ph. (614) 276-9302**

Interested In Buying

"Trench" Lighters and
Other Vintage or Unique Lighters

**Also Pre-1960 Zippo Pocket Lighters
With Advertising
and Zippo Table Lighters**

ELAINE'S TIQUES

**Wes & Elaine Hart
963 Westhaven St.
Columbus, OH 43228**

Ph. (614) 870-7141

CAN-A-DAY ANTIQUES

China • Glassware • Linens
Antiques and Collectibles

Phil and Shirley Canaday
624 Candlewood Dr.
Marion, IN 46952
Ph. (317) 664-3460

Animal Foot Rope lighter, 5¹/²".

The Matchless Lighter, Patented on
April 27, 1897; by USA and England Wesz
Mfg. Co. of Brooklyn NY, 2⁵/⁸".

Comet Wristwatch made in Japan, Box 3³/⁴".

Lid open showing cigarette depository.

Lid closed. Cigarette is dispensed from front opening- cigarette is lit.

Serv-A-Smok by Blake-Clarke Co., Sterling Silver is from Shrieve, Crump and Low Co. This item is made of very heavy Sterling Silver. Base 7$^{1/4''}$ x 5$^{1/4''}$, Item 5$^{1/2''}$ tall

Phil Canaday of Marion, IN owned this piece

Back of mechanical works, shows bellows that sucks flame to light cigarette.

Front of works showing flintwheel etc.

Bowers Peli-Can Lighter
with lable on it, 2³/⁴".

Bowers Peli-Can Lighter
with label on back side, 6¹/²" x 2³/⁴".

Peli-Can Advertising Display Lighter by Bowers,
2³/⁴" x 6¹/²".

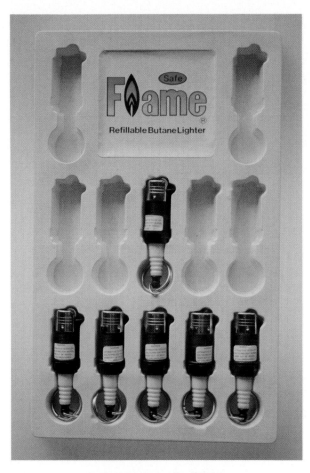

1993 display of refillable
Butane Lighters, 7" x 11½".

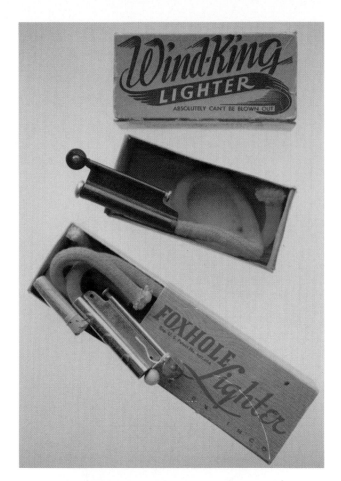

Top: Wind-King Lighter by Myron Gray,
mint in original box, 3¾" x 1¾".

Bottom: Foxhole Lighter by Imco,
mint in original box, 3¾" x 1¾".

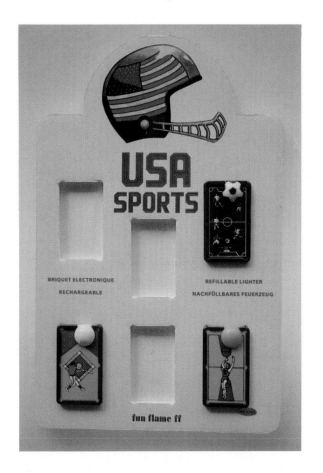

Refillable Sports Lighters on display (1993),
7¼" x 11".

1965 Zippo letter and envelope concerning a no charge policy on broken Zippos.

Top: Scripto Butane lighter tin, 3¹/₄" x 2¹/₄".
Bottom: Tin for Ronson Service Kit. Contains
package of igniters, fuel-fill capsule, spark wheel
brush, wick, inserter, and instruction booklet ,
3¹/₁₆" x 1⁷/₈".

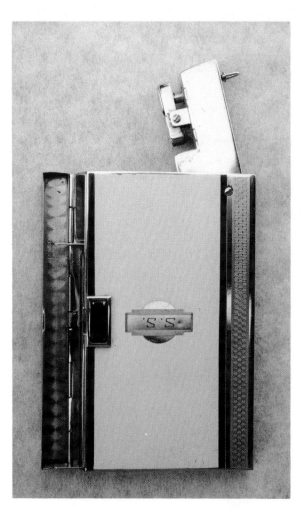

1930's Ronson-Art Metal Works
case and lighter combo, 4¹/²" x 3"

The Match King Westclox Tiny Time Striker,
made in Chicago, 4" x 5³/⁴".

Unmarked lighter with
Swiss Clock.

Plastic lighter and cigarette pack holder,
2³/⁴" x 1" x 3¹/⁴".

"Cig Top" lighter with a Lift-Arm. This item went into a pack of cigarettes, $3^{1/4}$" x $2^{1/4}$" x 3"

Pres-A-Lite Electric Car with a cigarette dispenser, and lighter. When pulled down on the bottom a cigarette comes down to light on an element, 4" x 3" x $3^{1/4}$".

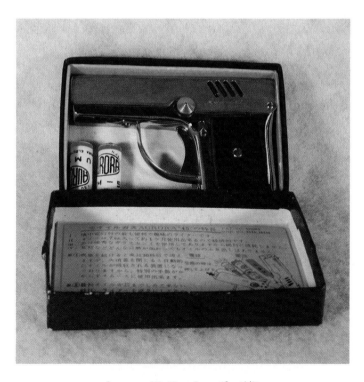

Table Lift-Arm the maker is unknown, 3" x $1^{3/4}$".

Aurora 45, Box Length $4^{1/4}$".

11

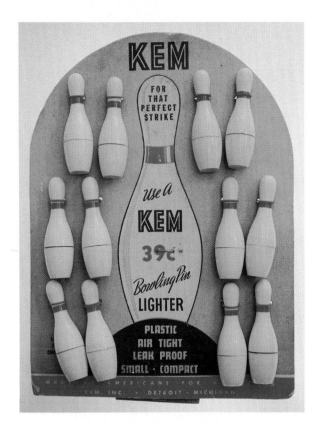

Display of Kem Bowling Pin Lighters,
Display 7³/₄" x 10¹/₄", Lighters-3" x ³/₄".

Evans Lighter Display Case with two levels and
the original velvet, 14" x 10¹/₂" x 4¹/₄".

Top-Marathon lighter, case, and compact combo,
Pat. No. 1921855, 3³/₄" x 2⁵/₈".

Bottom-Evans lighter, case, and compact combo,
Pat. No. 80179, 4³/₈" x 2¹/₄".

Ronson copper bulldog striker,
lighter and ashtray, 3¹/⁴" x 5" x 4".

1930's Ronson horse head striker, 4¹/²" x 5¹/²".

Ronson scotty dog striker, 3³/⁴" x 5¹/⁴".

Ronson elephant striker lighter,
2³/⁴" x 3³/⁴" x 5".

13

Ronson Touch-Tip and calendar pad, 9³/⁴".

1930's Ronson Monkey Pik-A-Cig Striker,
enameled box, Art Deco, 5" x 8³/⁸".

Ronson Touch-Tip and cigarette box, 8¹/²".

Ronson Touch-Tip bartender lighter.
Chrome and enamel, 7¹/₂".

Ronson Touch-Tip bartender lighter.
Enameled bar with cigarette holders
on each side, 6¹/₄" x 6³/₄".

1936 Ronson Touch-Tip Table Lighter
4" x 2¹/⁴" x 3¹/²".

1936 Ronson Touch-Tip sterling
silver lighter, 2¹/²" x 3³/⁴".

Oriental Man holding lighter. Made
in Occupied Japan, copper plated,
4¹/⁴".

Strikalite Lighter on elephant with an ashtray,
3³/⁴" x 5" x 2³/⁴".

Ronson Touch-Tip lighter
and clock combo, 3³/₄" x 4".

Ronson Touch-Tip lighter.
Chrome and tortoise enamel, 3¹/₄".

Ronson streamlined Touch-Tip lighter, 3¹/₂" x 4³/₈".

Ronson streamlined Touch-Tip lighter, 3¹/₂" x 4³/₈".

Ronson Touch-Tip table top lighter.

Ronson Touch-Tip lighter and pipe holder, 5" x 6³/⁴".

Ronson Touch-Tip lighter, 3¹/²" x 3¹/⁴".

Ronson Touch-Tip lighter.
Enamel and chrome, 3³/⁴" x 3".

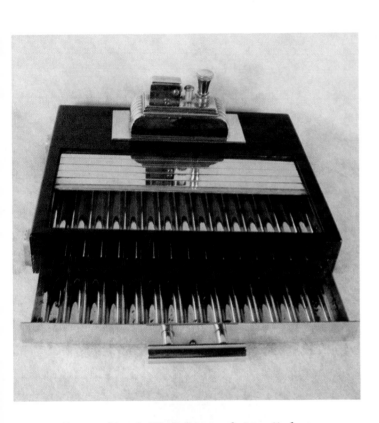

Ronson Touch-Tip lighter and cigarette box.
Rolltop chrome and enamel, 7¹/⁴" x 6".

Ronson Touch-Tip lighter and pipe holder, 7" x 4³/⁸".

Art Deco Elgin American lighter and
cigarette boxes, 8¹/²" x 3³/⁴" x 4".

Ronson Touch-Tip lighter, 3¹/₂" x 2¹/₂" x 3¹/₄".
(Square Touch-Tip)

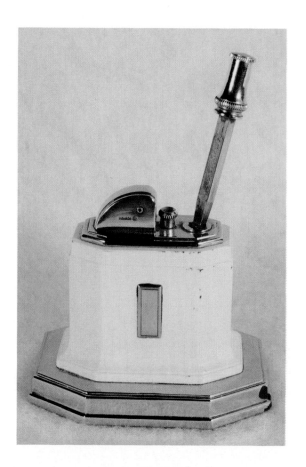

Ronson Touch-Tip table top lighter,
3¹/₂" x 2¹/₂" x 3¹/₄".
(Square Touch-Tip)

Ronson Touch Tip, 3¹/₂" x 2¹/₂" x 3¹/₄".
(Round Touch-Tip)

Ronson Touch-Tip, chrome and black,
3¹/₂" x 2¹/₂" x 3¹/₄".
(Round Touch-Tip)

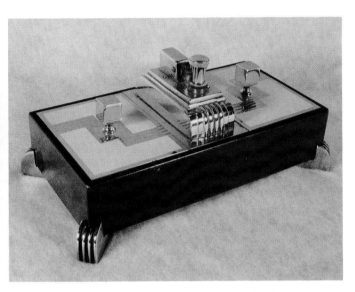

Ronson Touch-Tip lighter and cigarette boxes.
Black and cream enamel, Octette lighter, 12$^{1/4}$".

Ronson Touch-Tip lighter and cigarette boxes, 3$^{1/4}$" x 8".

Ronson Art Deco Touch-Tip lighter with cigarette boxes, 1" x 4" x 4".

Ronson Art Metal Works, copper
plated houndog striker, 4¹/²".

Ronson Striker, dachshund's tail pulls out, 4" x 9¹/²".

Ronson Monkey Striker, 3³/⁴".

Ronson Smoking Dog Striker, 5".

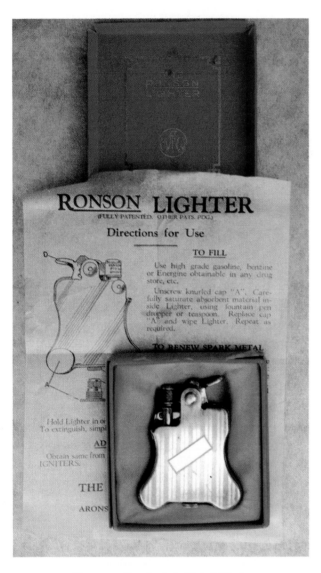

Ronson, Banjo Art Metal Works
silverplated lighter with original box
and instructions, 2¹/₄", Late 1920's .

Ronson Senator, sterling silver
Siam Shell, 2³/₈" x 3¹/₄", made in England.

Ronson "Gloria", 3³/₈" x 1⁷/₈".

1936 Flameless Cigarette Lighter made by Lektro Lite. Push button type lighter ignites coil inside plastic tube, fluid included. Lighter: $1/2$" x $2^{1/2}$", Box: $3^{1/2}$" x 3".

1937 Energine Cigar Lighter Fluid Can with metal spout made by The Cummer Products Co.

1924 Cenol Lighter Fluid Can with lead spout. Notice the lift-arm pictured on the can, made by Cenol Company, 5"

Ronsonol Lighter Fluid can
with lead spout, 2¹/²" x 5¹/²".

Ronsonol Lighter Fluid bottle, 6¹/²" x 2".

Ronsonol can, 5" x 2".

Ronson Wick and Inserters in original packages, 2¹/⁴" x 1¹/²".

Sunoco and Sohio Lighter Fluid cans both with
straight plastic spouts, both 4" x 2¹/₂".

Flick Lighter Fluid Can with lead
spout by Arrow Products, 6".

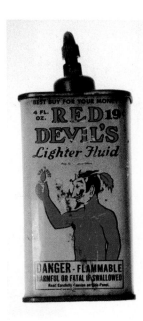

Red Devil Lighter
Fluid can, 4" x 2¹/₂".

Both Penn Champ Lighter Fluid
cans with straight plastic spout.

Sinclair, Ronsonol and Gulf Lighter Fluid
cans all with plastic spouts, Gulf -3¹/₄"
Ronsonol and Sinclair, 4³/₄".

Cardinal, Flying, and Flick Flash Lighter
Fluid with plastic spout, 5".

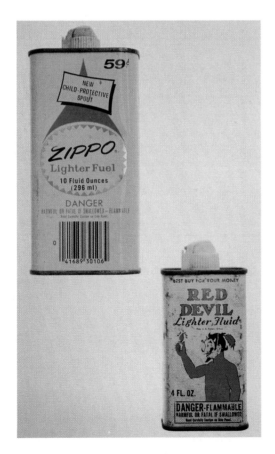

Zippo and Red Devil Lighter Fluid with
plastic spouts, Zippo 6", Devil 4¹/₂".

Shell Lighter Fluid cans,
Large 6", Small 4³/₄".

Wright Lighter Fluid can and box,
Can 1$^{1/2}$" x 3$^{1/2}$", Box 2$^{1/2}$" x 2$^{1/2}$" x 3$^{1/2}$".

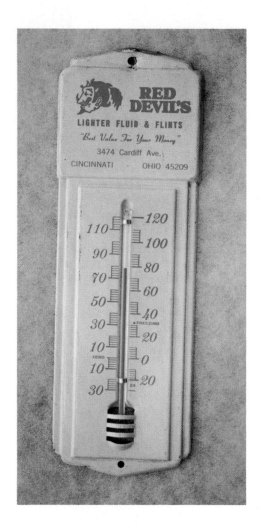

Advertising thermometer for Red Devil's
Lighter Fluid and Flints, 2$^{11/16}$" x 7$^{11/16}$".

Devil Laboratories lighter fluid dispenser for store
use with original can of Devil's Lighter Fluid inside,
Dispenser 5$^{1/4}$" x 8$^{3/4}$", Fluid Can 2$^{3/4}$" x 5$^{1/2}$".

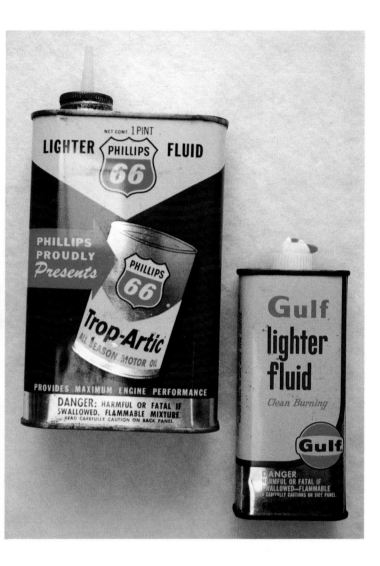

Left: Phillips 66 Lighter Fluid Can, $3^{7/8}$" x $7^{1/4}$".

Right: Gulf Lighter Fluid Can with a plastic spout, $2^{1/4}$" x $5^{1/2}$".

Top: The Pep Boys Lighter Fluid Can with a plastic spout, $5^{1/4}$".

Bottom: Penn-Jersey Auto Stores Inc. Lighter Fluid Can with a plastic spout, $5^{1/4}$".

1930 Firefly jewelry counter lighter fluid dispenser by Clark.

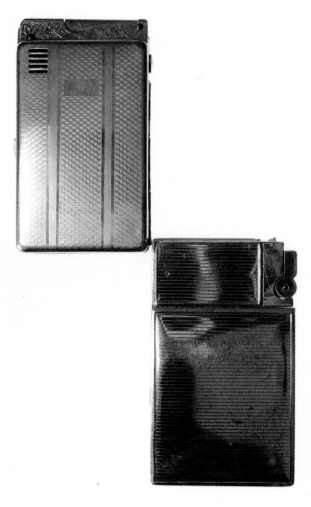

Top: "Atom" Terra Japan lighter and cigarette case made
in Occupied Japan, 2" x $^{1/2}$" x $3^{3/4}$".

Bottom: A.S.R. lighter and cigarette case, $2^{1/4}$" x $^{1/4}$" x 4".

1930's Evans compact and cigarette
lighter combo, $6^{5/8}$".

Metal Fields lighter and cigarette case with box,
3" x $^{1/2}$" x $4^{3/4}$".

Ronson Twenty Case Chromium Two-Tone
Tortoise Enamel E.T. model #32385, 3" x 4¹/₄".

Ronson DeLight Art Deco original case, cigarette
case and lighter set with a genuine chrome plate,
Lighter-1³/₄" x 1¹/₄", Case-4" x 2³/₄".

Ronson cigarette lighter combo,
Tortoise Style Enamel, 4¹/₄" x 3¹/₄".

Top Left: Evans lighter and cigarette case with
military emblem, 2⁵/₈" x 4¹/₂"
Top Right: Evans Trig-A-Lite" lighter and cigarette
case, 2⁵/₈" x 4¹/₄"
Bottom: Ronson "King" lighter and cigarette case
with original box, 2⁵/₈" x ⁷/₈"

Ronson Ten-A-Case Chromium Tortoise
mint in box, model #33415, 3³/₈" x 4¹/₈".

Ronson King Mastercase Chromium Butler Polished
E.T. mint in box, model #81150, 2¹/₂" x 4³/₄".

Ronson Mastercase Chromium E.T. Tortoise Enamel
mint in box, model #26379, 2³/₄" x 4³/₈".

Ronson Ten-A-Case, Chromium Tortoise
mint in box, model #33419, 3³/₈" x 4¹/₈".

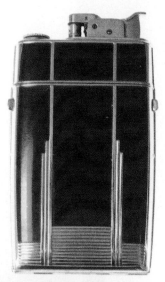

Evans Trig-A-Lite lighter and cigarette case,
Lighter-1$^{1/2}$" x 2", Case-2$^{7/8}$" x 3$^{7/8}$".

Top: Art Deco Evans lighter and cigarette case,
2$^{1/4}$" x $^{1/2}$" x 4$^{1/4}$".

Bottom: Art Deco Ronson lighter and cigarette combo,
4$^{3/4}$" x $^{3/8}$" x 3".

Floral Pattern with Tortoise
Style Enamel, 3$^{1/4}$".

Black Enamel, 4$^{1/4}$".

Evans wood and metal gas lighter, 3" x 4".

Lights and Roses table lighter with box.
Made by Teeco of Japan, 2" x 1¼" x 3¼".

Evans Bone China lighter, 3" x 2".

Table lighter by Myflam with silver relief,
3½" x 1⅝" x 2¾".

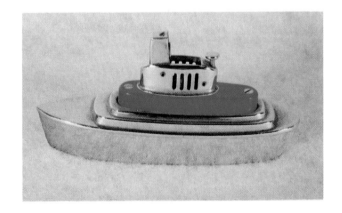

Occupied Japan, 4⅝" x 2".

Little Dorgento lighter with pictorial relief,
3" x 1¹/⁴" x 3".

Sunliter cigarette lighter with original box
and instructions, 4³/⁴" x 3¹/⁴".

Left: Catalin lighter made in Japan, 1¹/⁴" x 2".

Right: CMG Table Lighter, 2¹/²" x 2¹/⁴".

Left: Weston Stove lighter, 1¹/²" x 3¹/⁴".

Right: Unknown lighter, 1³/⁴" x 3¹/²".

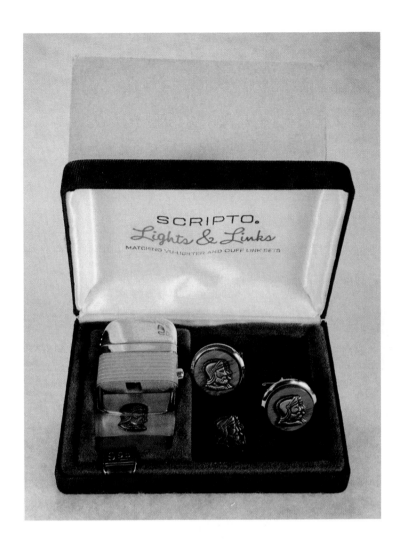

Scripto Vu-Lighter with matching cuff links and tie tack in original case.

Case: 4³/₄" x 3¹/₄"
Lighter: 1³/₈" x 2¹/₂"

1956 Chase Art Deco Lighter,
1³/₄" x 3¹/₄".

Unknown maker. A Leatherette
Cover is on the lighter, 1³/₈" x 3".

Scripto Vu-Lighter made in
Atlanta, USA. Hard to find table
top lighter, 4³/₈" x 2³/₄".

Ronson nude figure with marbleized base and a New Yorker insert,
12" x 11".

USA Strike-A-Lite perfume
bottle sytle, 3".

Occupied Japan Elephant Lighter.

Porcelain Japan lighter, 3¹/₄".

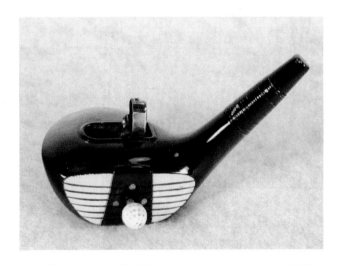

Golfclub and golfball lighter maker unknown, 3¹/₄".

Ronson Art Pottery lighter is a set including
an ashtray and lighter, 3" x 3"

Sheild's Model T Ford made in Japan,
2^{7/8"} x 4^{7/8"}.

Art Deco Tray made in the U.S.A. with a
Japanese Arrow Lighter, 5^{3/4"}.
The lighter is removable.

Unknown lighter marked on the
bottom "A Lion on top of AE".
The lighter came with an ashtray
and a cigarette dispenser, 2" x 3".

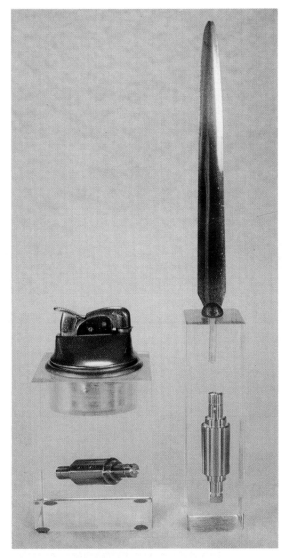

Occupied Japan table lighter is designed by Chase, (part of a three piece set which includes a lighter, tray and cigarette holder,) 3$^{1/4}$" x 2$^{3/4}$".

Evans Lucite lighter and letter opener set. The lighter is 2$^{1/4}$" x 4" and the opener is 1" x 8".

Occupied Japan C.M.C. silverplated lighter 3$^{3/8}$".

"Strik-A-Lite" wood mallard duck lighter, 4" x 1$^{3/4}$" x 2$^{1/2}$".

Table top lighter with a copper color made in Negbaur, NY; 2$^{1/4}$".

Japan Sailboat, 8$^{1/4}$".

"Monte Carlo" lighter made in Japan, 3" x 5$^{1/4}$".

Ski Blade and Shoe lighter
by Olympic, 8$^{1/2}$" x 1$^{1/2}$" x 2$^{1/2}$".

Musical Reel to Reel lighter,
Made in Japan, 4" x 4" x 1$^{5/8}$".

1910 Ford Lighter made in Japan 3¹/⁴".

Kroydon "Score Lite," stainless steel pocket
lighter. Push button mechanism on side
keeps track of scoring, 2¹/₂" x 1¹/₂".

Evans Table Lighter, sterling silver,
2" x 3".

1950 Stainless Steel Table Lighter,
1¹/₂" x 3¹/₂".

Swank clock and calendar,
Japan, 8¹/₄" x 2³/₄".

Left: Japan marbleized coat, 3¹/₂" x 1¹/₂".
Right: Bakelite, USA, 3¹/₂" x 1³/₄".

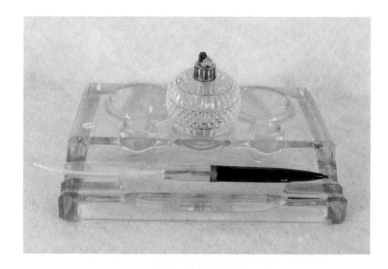

Desktop lighter, pen, and inkwell set, glass,
maker unknown, 6³/₄".

Gas Pump, Occupied Japan,
3¹/₂" x 2¹/₄".

Fire Bellows, Japan, unknown maker, 7" x 3" x 1¹/₂".

1934 Advertising Bar Lighter, 7$^{1/2}$" x 10$^{1/4}$" x 11".

Akro Agate electric lighter with an ashtray base. Made by Vidrio Products Corp. in Cicero, IL. 2$^{1/8}$" x 2$^{5/8}$".

1962 Electric Clock lighter made by Timelite, 6" x 4$^{3/4}$" x 4$^{1/2}$".

Electric Table Lighter made from bakelite and metal. When lifted heating element is triggered. Made in the USA, 3$^{1/4}$" x 2$^{1/2}$".

Evans Bone China and
gold detailed lighter, 3" x 4".

Left: German Glass lighter, Japan, 4" x 6".
Right: Blue Glass, Penguin lighter, Japan, 2¹/⁴" x 4".

Brown and Bigelow Lighter,
marked Remembrance from Brown and Bigelow,
5¹/²" x 2¹/⁴" x 1¹/²".

Evans advertising lighter, "RCA Tubes",
lucite, 1⁷/⁸" x 3¹/⁴".

Hy Glo with sterling casing, USA, 2" x 2¹/²".

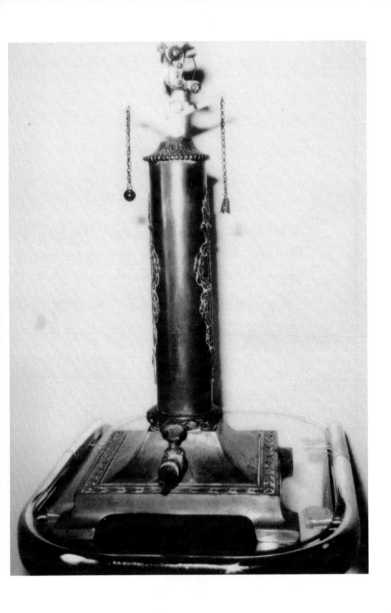

Bradley and Hubbard Table Lighter.
Torch embossing on vertical tube.
Ignited by pulling on chains, 7" x 7" x 13$^{1/2}$".
(Probably made at the turn of the century).

Brown and Bigelow Ships Wheel,
(*Note* broken striking handle).
Advertising F.M. Lowry and Son
Walton, Indiana, "4" x 4".

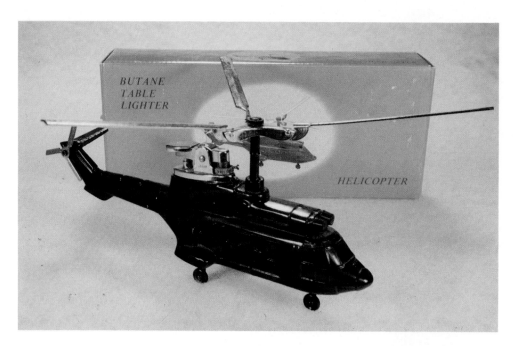

Two 1986 Butane novelty helicopter lighters made in Japan. One of the lighters is still in the original box, both are 8" x 1¹/²" x 3¹/²".

Ritepoint lighter by Scripto,
2" x 4¹/²".

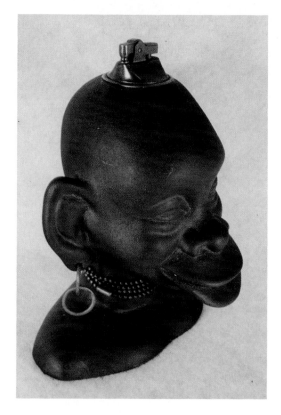

Ceramic African head made in Japan, 8¹/²".

Left: Super Deluxe table lighter made by ATC,
3¹/₂" x 1¹/₂" x 3".

Right: 1975 Fitz and Floyd, Inc. Japanese lighter, 2" x 3".

Ronson "Vara-Flame Luralite"
table lighter, 2³/₄" x 3".

Occupied Japan lighter-2¹/₂" x 1¹/₂" x 2³/₄".

Chrome ball lighter made in Japan.

Chrome ruler made in Japan, 13".

Evans Smoking Set including a lighter, ashtray, and a cigarette holder.
lighter- 3", ashtray-5$^{3/4}$", cigarette holder-2$^{3/4}$"

Ronson sterling siver Jubilee
table lighter, 1$^{7/8}$" x 3$^{3/4}$".

Augusta table lighter made in
West Germany, 3" x 1$^{3/4}$" x 2$^{1/2}$".

Political lighters made by Amico of Japan,
2$^{1/8}$".

(closed)　　　　　　　　　　　　　　　　　　(open)

"Lucky Key" lighter, 1³/⁴"

1930 Bakelite Beer Bottle Lighter, ³/⁴" x 3"

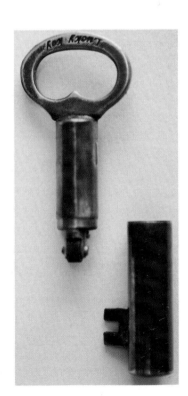

(closed)　　　　　　　　　　　　　　　　　　(open)

Ellis Bakelite Table Lighter, 3³/⁴" x 1³/⁴" x 6"

(open)

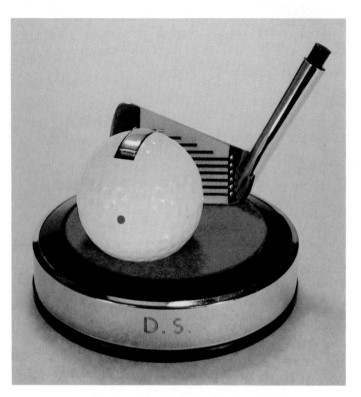

Swank golf club and golfball lighter made in Japan, "Nov. 20, 1966 is engraved on the back. To trigger the lighter in the golfball push the button on top of the club. 5$^{1/2}$" x 4$^{3/4}$"

Evans silverplated cigarette holder and lighter, 8$^{3/4}$".

Slot machine by Bently Gifts, Inc. of N. Bellmore NY. Patented by Japan, 4$^{1/2}$" x 3".

Japanese lighter and cigarette holder, 6" x 4$^{1/4}$".

Brass bell with an oversized
lighting mechanism, 5".

Occupied Japan Wond-O-Lite
cigarette lighter and holder, 3¹/₂".

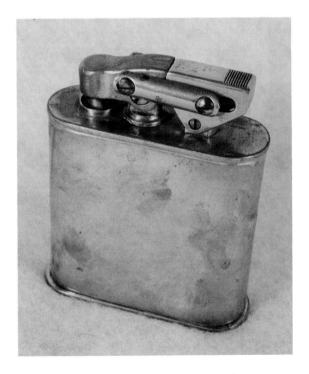

Swank wood and metal lighter made in Japan, 10" x 3³/₄".

Brass pocket lighter, maker is unknown.
This picture is enlarged in contrast to
the other pictures, 4" x 3¹/₄".

Electric Push-Button table lighter,
Base-2$^{1/4}$" x 5" Top-1".

Electric Bakelite lighter and cigarette pack holder with
original box by the Tarrson Co. of Chicago, IL;
2$^{3/4}$" x 2" x 4".

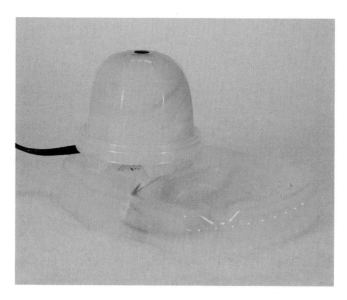

Akro Agate Electric Lighter with an ashtray base,
Ashtray-2$^{1/2}$" x 2$^{1/4}$", Lighter-5$^{1/4}$" x 4" x $^{3/8}$".

Manning-Bowman and Co. table electric
lighter Patented on June 20, 1911;
3$^{1/2}$" x 3$^{1/2}$" x 6$^{1/2}$".

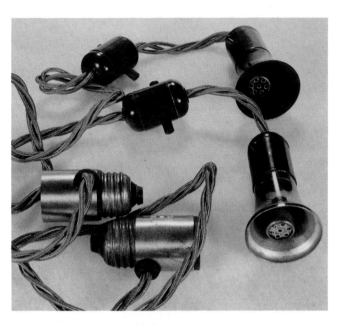

Electric lamp lighters that work by screwing a light bulb on the top and then the unit must be screwed into a light bulb receptical, 1³/⁴" x 3¹/²".

Lamp-O-Lighter's by A.W. Frankling Inc. of New York City, 1¹/²" x 3" (cord 2").

TASSEL-LITER

the electric smoke lighter concealed in the tassle of a silk lamp pull-cord

TASSEL-LITER

$3.00

Tassel-Liter with original box, 1" x 3" (cord 18").

Electric lighter in the original unused
package. Copyright in 1964 by Japan,
10$^{1/4}$".

Elec-Tray by Cobb Metal Products Corp.
in Smyrna, GA; 7$^{3/4}$".

Cast aluminum electric dog lighter.

Electric Mircophone the maker
is unknown, 2$^{1/4}$" x 3".

Ship Captain's head his pipe is the lighter and his eyes glow.
This piece mounts on the wall, 8" x 2" x 8".

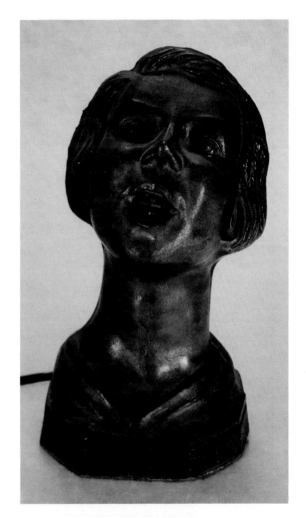

Bronze plated lady's head electric lighter
4" x 4" x 8".

Fisherman Captain electric lighter,
$2^{1/2}$" x $4^{1/4}$".

Electric microphone, 7$^{1/4}$" x 5$^{1/8}$".

Porcelain drunken man electric lighter, 4" x 2" x 4".

Porcelain electric lighter by Eagle, 2$^{1/8}$" x 2$^{1/4}$".

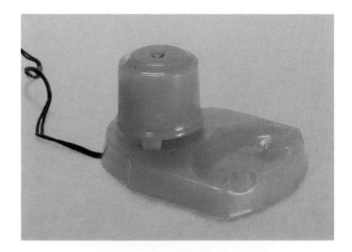

Green Akro Agate electric lighter and
ashtray base, 5" x 4" x 3".

Majestic electric lighter with box made by
Keilson Cigar Co. in Cincinnati, OH; $2^{7/8}$" x $4^{1/2}$".

Electric Bakelite Art Deco Lighter,
4" with no markings.

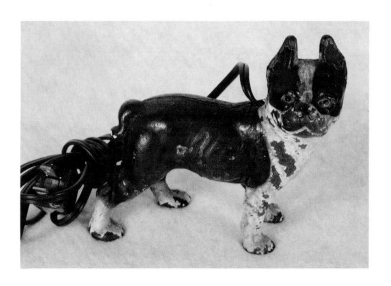

Electric Iron bulldog, $5^{1/4}$" x $4^{7/8}$".

Electric, glass and amber lighter with a
firefly shape, $4^{3/4}$"

Round electric lighters.

Curtis Pop Up lighter similar to an
auto lighter, plugs into a 110 outlet.

1937 Electric Cigarette Valet, made in the USA
by NYC Asterbilt Products Corp., 2⁵/₈" x 4³/₄".

Electric lighter with no marks,
2³/₄" x 2".

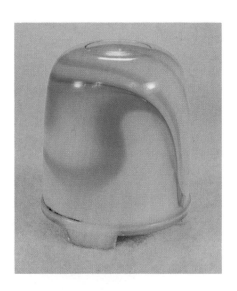

Green Akro Agate electric lighter,
2" x 2¹/₂".

Electric Egyptian woman electric lighter
made from pot metal, 6³/⁴".

Electric Sunbeam Smokemaster the cigarette
is automatically lit made in Chicago, 4" x 7³/⁴".

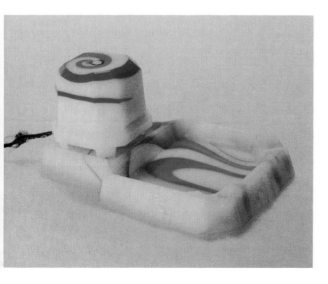

Akro Agate electric lighter with an ashtray
5" x 4" x 2³/⁴".

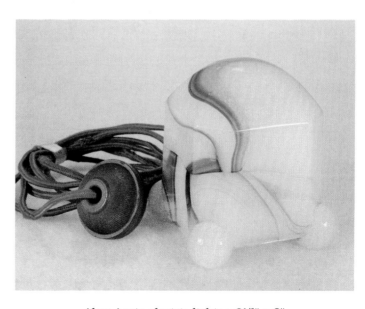

Akro Agate electric lighter, 2¹/²" x 3".

West Germany lighter on Resin Art Metal base marked Saschab, a California Art Pottery Company, came with an ashtray, 2" x 4".

Left: Wooden table lighter made in Japan, 2¹/²" x 5¹/²".

Right: G.S. table lighter made in Japan, 2" x 5".

Brass lighter made in Austria, 2¹/²" x 1¹/⁴", U.S. Patent April 2, 1912.

Colibri table lighter by Kreisler, 2¹/⁴" x 4".

Daltis 24k gold plated, Thorens Swiss made, 4" x 1¹/⁴".

Japanese Lighter, 3¹/²" x 1¹/²".

Evans hand enameled two piece set, 3³/⁴".

Both are Evans table lighters, 2¹/⁴" x 1¹/⁴" x 5".

Evans table lighter, 3" x 2".

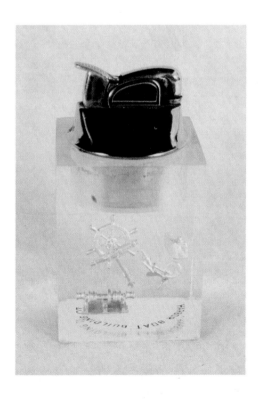

Nautical Theme Lighter with clear plastic
base and a Japanese Insert.

Brass cigarette lighter, Swiss made,
3¹/₈" x 2" x 2¹/₂".

Evans Bone China lighter with gold pinstriping, 4¹/₂" x 4".

Left: Lamp Post Lighter, 9¹/₂" x 3".

Right: Evans table lighter, 2¹/₄" x 7¹/₂".

Electric gas lighter made to look like a torch. Made by Pyro-Star in Japan, 4^1/2" x 3^1/4" x 5".

Electric Figural gas table lighter by Tsukushi of Japan, 3^1/2" x 9".

Prince gas lighter made in Japan, 4".

Early model of the Dunhill Tinder Pistol, 6¼" x 4".

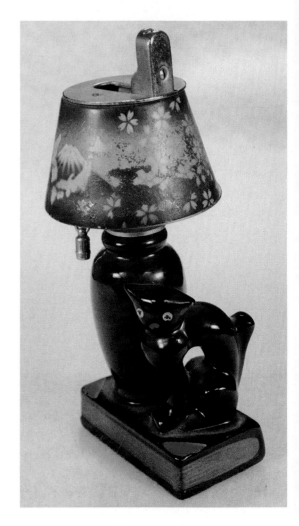

Lamp lighter made in Japan, 2½" x 2½" x 5½".

Evans Inserts and ashtrays, original sticker
price in bronze color, $15.95, 9".

Music box and lighter combo made in Japan.
The turntable moves 4".

1958 Zippo fashioned by Roseart Co. of
Bradford, PA; 3" x 2" x 4³/₄" Made
of brass and marble.

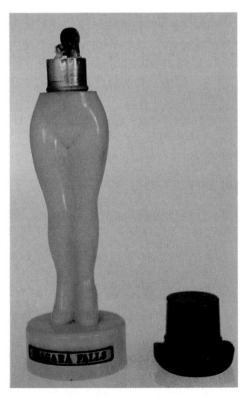

Plastic "Miss Cutie" lighter by Negbaur of NY.

Dunhill silverplated
ruler, made in
England

Sterling Silver Lighter with alcohol,
cigar cutter and an ashtray, 5".

Dunhill Bumper lighter in the original box,
made in England, $2^{7/8}$" x $2^{1/8}$"

Japan two piece lighter and ashtray souvenir, $3^{1/2}$".

Two Knight Table Top Lighters by Negbaur.

Ram Striker, 2⁵/₈" x 3³/₄".

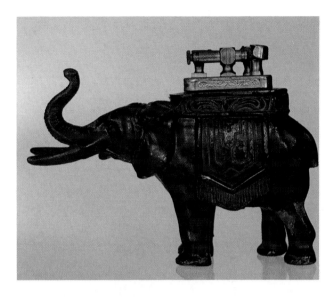

Cast Aluminum painted Flip-Top elephant lighter,
4³/₄" x 1¹/₄" x 3¹/₂".

Cannon lighter by Negbaur, 8" x 3" x 2¹/₂".

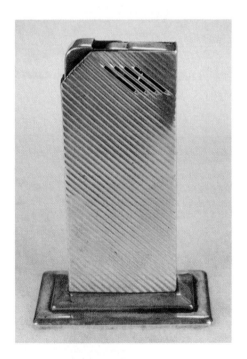

Tiffany and Co. sterling silver
table lighter, "Pat. #RE 19023
Expires June 1952".

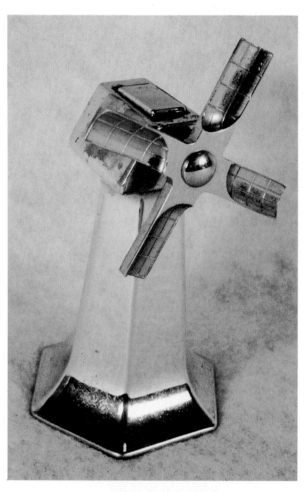

Windmill made by Bu-Wel Metal Products
of Bangor, Michigan; 5"

Dunhill Tinder Box with pistol, 5$^{1/2}$" x 1$^{1/2}$" x 3$^{1/4}$".

Chrome Plane lighter and ashtray
made by Occupied Japan, 6$^{3/4}$" x 7$^{1/2}$" x 5".

Two Catalin Bakelite Lighters the
maker is unknown, 4$^{1/4}$" x 1$^{1/2}$".

Electric Self Starting Timelite by
Alba Art in Chicago, 4¼" x 7".

Enameled Baggage Cart with a lighter, ashtray,
cigarette holder, and rubber wheels, 3¾" x 4½".

Occupied Japan fan, 3¼".

Musical Knight Set with a match box holder,
cigarette holder, lighter, and two ashtrays;
cigarette holder, 2¾"; ashtrays, 3¼";
lighter, 3¼"; knight, 9".

Music Box with a cigarette holder and lighter,
made by Tuyo Company of Japan, 3" x 5¼".

Painted Cast Aluminum ashtray and lighter,
6" x 5$^{1/2}$" x 4".

Dog with head off.

Park Table Top Lighter.

Lamp Lighter made in Japan,
4" x 2".

Occupied Japan Lighter and
Calendar, 4$^{1/4}$" x 1$^{7/8}$".

Alcohol with wand, 2³/₄"

Store Cigar continuous lighted lighter with
three Perma Wicks, 6" x 2¹/₂" x 4¹/₂".

Mosda Period Series sterling silver lighter,
3¹/₂" x 2" x 2¹/₄".

R. K. lighter made in Austria, 3" x 1" x 3".

Knapp cigarette holder and lighter, 3¹/₄" x 1³/₄".

Table Lift-Arm with a gold plated
top and the rest of the item is pot
metal, no markings, 5³/₄".

Brass Lift-Arm lighter,
2" x 3³/₄".

Brass Hamburg, ashtray
with a striker and a cigar cutter,
6⁵/₈" x 5³/₄".

Iron with Evans Insert, 9¹/₄".

Countertop Cigar Cutter and Alcohol Burner,
made out of glass and brass, 3³/₄" x 4³/₄".

Glass base with brass shade marked "Gesch."

Lamp with shade on

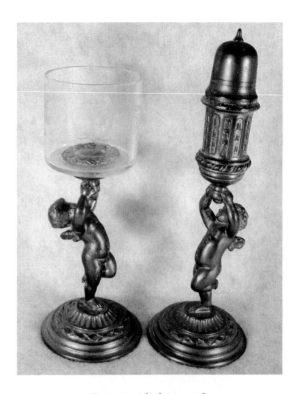

Pairpoint lighter with
etched glass cigarette holder, 8¹/₂".

Brass lighter with cigarette holder and ashtray,
made in Austria, 4¹/₂" x 5³/₄"

Brass lighter marked "562 L. Germany", 4" x 5".

All copper Capitol lighter, base is marked
"Mfg. by Steele and Johnsonn Mfg. Co.
Essenjoy Products," Patented Sept. 17, 1912;
5" x 2⁷/₈".

1928 Apollo, Elks Lodge Anniversary
Coffee Urn, 4¹/₂" x 2¹/₄".

1925 lighter and ashtray.

Occupied Japan Sister Sewing Machine with
lighter and cigarette holder, 2³/⁴" x 3³/⁴".

Unmarked Table Top lighter
with mirrored sides.

Everflow, 4¹/⁸" x 2³/⁸".

Tiffany and Company lighter with
sterling silver base, 2¹/⁴" x 3".

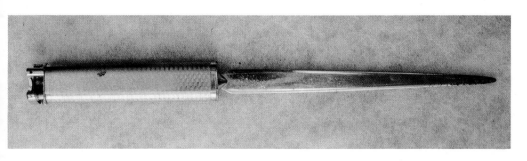

Dunhill letter opener with
Lift-Arm combo, ³/⁴" x 8⁵/⁸".

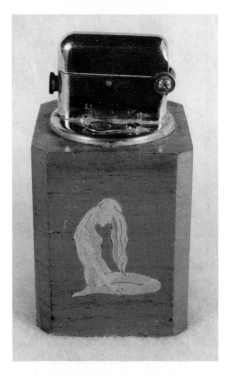

Art Deco Lady on a wood base
with a Thorens Insert.

Bakelite Lift-Arm Lighter with an
unknown manufacturer,
2$^{1/2}$" x 2" x 3$^{1/4}$".

Thorens of Switzerland Lighter on
stone base, 2$^{1/2}$" x 3$^{1/4}$".

Hand painted vase decoration
lighter with Thorens Insert.

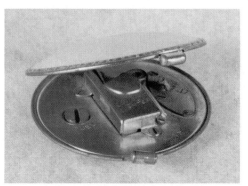

Plaza enameled lighter, made in the USA
with a compact shape, 2$^{1/4}$".

Made in the USA in a rare form, 3¹/₈" x 5³/₄".

Brass "Spirit of St. Louis"
Table Lighter made by Swank.

Occupied Japan car with friction wheels, 4⁷/₈" x 1⁵/₈".

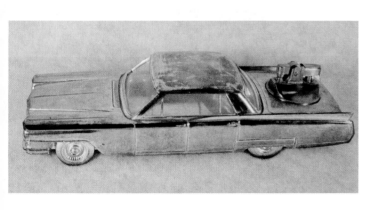

Japan lighter and cigarette holder, 9¹/₈".

No markings 7³/₄" x 3³/₄".

Bradford (Lady) Zippo Table Lighter,
2¹/⁴" x 1¹/²" x 3¹/²".

Corinthian Zippo Lighter, was
discontinued in 1966,
2¹/²" x 4".

Zippo Table Lighter,
2" x 1¹/²" x 3¹/⁴".

Zippo Table Lighter with engraving
"1950-3rd Barcroft Full Zippo
Insert", 2" x 1¹/²" x 3¹/⁴".

Kaschie lighter made in Germany-U.S. Zone, 5$^{1/2}$".

G.B. Co. of Joliet, IL; Pat. Sept. 17, 1912;
brass with a wood base, 5$^{1/2}$".

Typewriter made in Occupied Japan, 3$^{3/4}$" x 1$^{7/8}$".

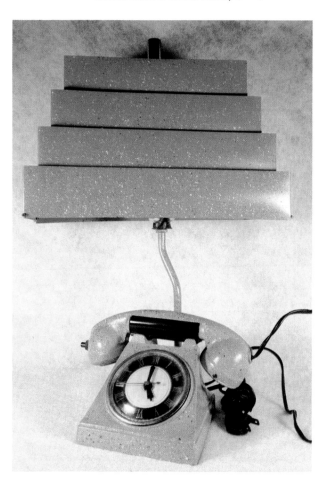

Art Deco clock, lamp, and lighter made by
The Trea-Boye Corp. of Brooklyn, NY; 17$^{1/4}$".

Evans enameled egg, 6¹/²".

Dunhill Silent Flame, battery operated, brass lighter, 7³/⁴" x 4³/⁴".

Crowned Lion with alcohol burner and wand in head, silver-plated, 3³/⁴" x 3¹/⁴".

Striker and brass cigarette pack holder made in Germany, 4" x 7".

Made out of potmetal,
made in Austria, 5³/8".

Zippo Table Model, Pat #2517191
® Pat #2940286, 4" x 2¹/4".

Dunhill Silent Flame, chrome plated
battery operated. Made in the USA,
3³/4" x 2³/4"

1945 Table Top lighter, with
tortoise color enamel, 3⁵/8".

Evans Trig-A-Lite lighter with
Lucky Strike advertising, $1^{1/2}$" x $^{1/2}$" x 2".

Musical lighter in the original box advertising
the Yellow Pages. This lighter was made
in Japan, $1^{3/4}$" x $^{3/4}$" x $2^{1/2}$".

Top: 1950 Zippo with Wurlitzer Phonograph
Music advertising, $1^{1/2}$" x $^{1/2}$" x $2^{1/4}$".
Bottom: Ronson "Windite" advertisng RCA,
$1^{1/2}$" x $^{1/2}$" x 2"

Brass Harley Davidson Lift-Arm lighter,
$1^{1/4}$" x $1^{7/8}$" x $^{1/2}$".

Top: Copper book lighter made in Japan,
1¹/⁴" x ¹/⁴" x 1¹/²".

Bottom: Coin type lighter made in Japan,
7" x 1¹/²" x ³/⁸".

Top Left: Butane "Windflame" pocket lighter
Made in Japan by Kay Woodie
2¹/⁴" x 1¹/⁴".

Top Right: Modern DeLuxe pocket lighter
made in Japan, 2³/¹⁶" x 1¹/⁴".

Bottom Left: Ronson Adonis pocket lighter
with purple cloth cover, 2³/¹⁶" x 1⁷/⁸"

Bottom Right: Lord Chesterfield pocket
lighter made in Japan, 2" x 1⁷/⁸"

All Scripto Vu-Lighters except bottom one which
is a Craftsman "Vista" from Japan.

#1,2, and 3- $1^{3/4}$" x $2^{3/4}$"

#4- $1^{3/8}$" x $2^{1/2}$"

#5- $1^{5/8}$" x $2^{1/4}$"

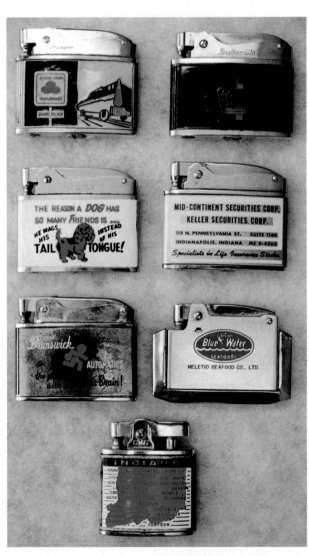

#1 Little Billboard of Japan advertising State
Farm Insurance, $2^{1/8}$" x $1^{7/8}$".

#2 Brother-Lite of Japan advertising the
Holiday Inn, $2^{1/8}$" x $1^{3/4}$".

#3 Firefly Super Lighter of Japan, $2^{1/8}$" x $1^{3/4}$".

#4 Wellington Balboa of Japan advertising
Mid-Continent Securities Corp. and Keller
Securities Corp., $2^{1/8}$" x $1^{3/4}$".

#5 Rosen Enterprises, Ltd of Japan, $2^{1/8}$" x $1^{3/4}$"
Brunswick Automatics, $2^{1/8}$" x $1^{3/4}$"

#6 Pocket and table lighter combo Cherry Lite
Auto TKC Slide of Japan advertising Blue
Water, $2^{3/8}$" x $1^{3/4}$".

#7 Continental CMC advertising Indiana,
$1^{5/8}$" x 2".

#1 Brass lighter by Craftsman of Japan with golfer, 1¹/²" x 2¹/⁴".

#2 Scripto Butane Lighter, 1³/⁸" x 2¹/²".

#3 Mastercraft lighter with a baseball player made in Japan, 1¹/⁴" x 2".

#4 Nimrod "Commander", 1³/⁸" x 2³/⁸".

#5 Idealine lighter with advertising made in Japan, 1¹/⁴" x 2".

#6 Stormking lighter with Florida State University advertising.

#7 "Life-Liter" a division of Ritepoint Pen and Pencil Co.", Zippo look-a-like, 1¹/²" x 2¹/⁴".

#1 Solo Deluxe pocket lighter by Imco, 1¹/²" x 2¹/⁴".

#2 Lord Chesterfield pocket lighter made in Japan, 1³/⁴" x 2¹/⁴".

#3 Marxman Windproof pocket lighter made in Japan, 1¹/²" x 2¹/⁴".

#4 Ronson "Typhoon" lighter marked on bottom of lighter "British Empire Made," has Vietnam engraving, 1¹/²" x 2¹/⁴".

#5 Ronson pocket lighter made in West Germany, 1¹/²" x 2⁵/⁸".

#6 Lektrolite pocket lighter, 1⁵/⁸" x 2".

Top Left: AIPCO of Japan with leather metal design, 2" x 1¹/²".

Top Right: Stratton "Augusta Lighter" made in West Germany, 1⁷/⁸" x 1³/⁸".

Middle Left: Japan lighter with leather and metal design, 2⁷/⁸" x 1¹/⁴".

Middle Right: Gold Tone lighter of Japan, 1¹¹/¹⁶" x 1¹/⁴".

Bottom: Japan lighter with leather design, 2⁷/⁸" x 1¹/⁴"

1984 Zippo with "U.S.S. Edson"
design on the front side.
1¹/²" x ¹/²" x 2¹/⁴"

Top: Regeliter with a push
button spring mechanisim
is a jewled lighter.

Bottom: A.S.R. pocket lighter

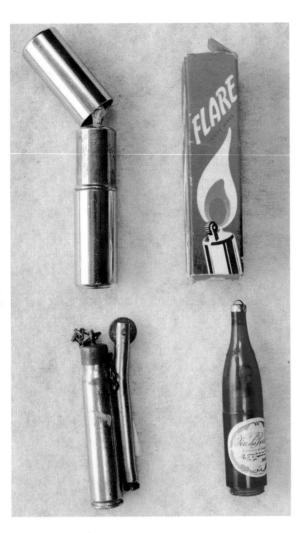

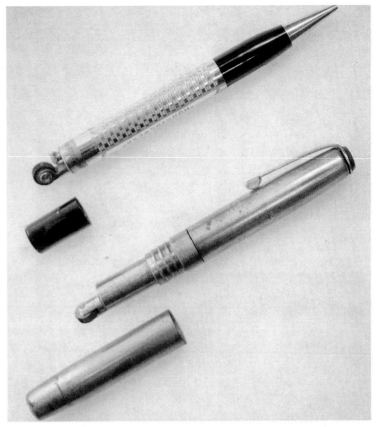

Top: "Munsing Wear" marked on pencil/lighter combo, 1/4" x 41/2".
Bottom: Waldrof brass lighter/pen combo, 1/2" x 41/2".

Top: Flare brand lighter with original box by Taber Bunshnell and Co., 2 13/16" x 5/8".

Bottom Left: Bullet type lighter, 2 3/4" x 7/8".

Bottom Right: Champagne Bottle made in Hong Kong, 9/16" x 2 3/4".

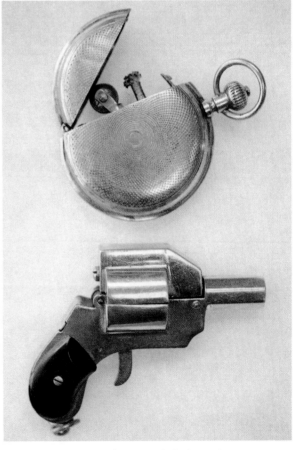

Sterling Silver Case with Zippo insert, (1947-1951). Marked "Thainnkon-Sterling", made in Siam.

Art Deco Evans "Trig-A-Lite".

Top: Pocket Watch lighter, 2".
Bottom: Pistol lighter with Thorens mechanisim, made in Austria by E and JB, 3" x 3/4" x 2".

Left: 1965 Zippo lighter with original box, advertising "Sherman Super Sonic Systems".

Right: Zippo "Rip-Off" "Hi-Lite" ligher with original box, advertising "Jamestown Metal Polishing"

Both-1$^{1/2}$" x $^{1/2}$" x 2$^{1/4}$"

These Zippo's are all advertising "F.I.S.H. Thanx".

Lighters-1$^{1/2}$" x $^{1/2}$" x 2$^{1/4}$"
Ruler-1$^{1/2}$" x $^{1/2}$" x 1$^{5/8}$"

Top: 1981 Zippo with box

Bottom Left: 1986

Bottom Right: Zippo Ruler

Zippo's

#1 Chrome with leatherette covering, 1976.

#2 Chrome, 1959 with engraving.

#3 Chrome, 1981 with engraving.

#4 1971 with fishing scene.

#5 1976 with advertising.

#6 1964 with advertising.

#7 1945 WWII, black crackle finish with original box.

Zippo's, 1 1/2" x 1/2" x 2 1/4"

#1 1965 advertising "Irving Concrete Corp.".

#2 1970 advertising Sumitville Bank and Trust Co.".

#3 1966 advertising "Richard L. Wagner Realtor".

#4 1940's engraved "RAHKE.

#5 1973 advertising "Indiana Tank Co.".

#6 1969 advertising "Magaw Corp.".

#7 1968 advertising "Nifda".

#8 1964 advertising "Parti-Barge".

#9 1959 advertising "Kopy-Kat".

Top: Dunhill "Unique" sterling silver
Lift-Arm lighter.
Bottom: Mara Man Baroque
silver plated Batone lighter – model #GL-57.

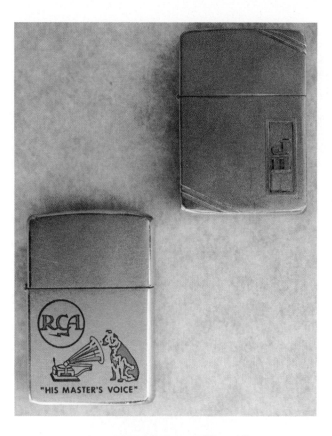

Top: Zippo lighter 2$^{1/8}$" x 1$^{1/2}$".
Bottom: Zippo advertising RCA,
dated April 1966 on back, 2$^{1/4}$" x 1$^{1/2}$".

No markings, 2" x 1$^{1/2}$".

Zippo "Black Crackle" 1943 pocket lighter.

Belgium Lift-Arm, Mercrius, 1$^{3/4}$".

Top Left: Aluminum lighter by Jola $^{3/4}$" x $2^{5/8}$".

Top Right: Aluminum lighter by Signal-U-Mfg. Co., $1^{1/8}$" x $2^{1/2}$".

Bottom: Polished aluminum lighter with 1945 Quarter, $1^{1/4}$" x $1^{3/4}$" x $^{5/8}$".

Two Dunhill service lighters.

Top lighter has originial box.

Bottom lighter advertising
The Pierce Governor Co., Inc.
in Anderson, Indiana.

Both lighters are $^{1/2}$" x $2^{1/4}$".

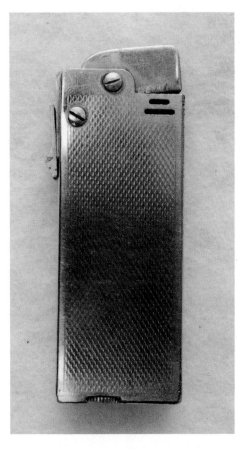

Thorens Swiss made pocket lighter,
$1^{1/8}$" x $2^{3/4}$".

Small Book Striker,
marked "The Light That Never Failed,"
unknown maker, $^{3/4}$" x $1^{1/2}$".

Brass Pocket Striker, maker unknown, 3".

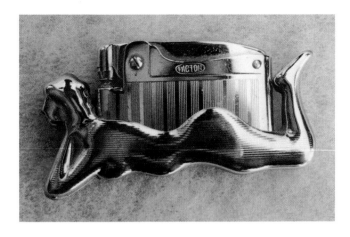

Japan pocket figural lighter, 2³/⁴".

German Gun Lighter,
marked "GFS. Geschutzt"

Siam Sterling, 2¹/⁴".

VIETNAM
PLEIKU
67-68

YEA THOUGH I WALK
THROUGH THE VALLEY
OF THE SHADOW OF
DEATH I WILL FEAR NO
EVIL FOR I AM THE
EVILEST SON OF A BITCH
IN THE VALLEY

Zenith "Wind Proof" pipe lighter
with Vietnam engraving.

Art Deco lighter.

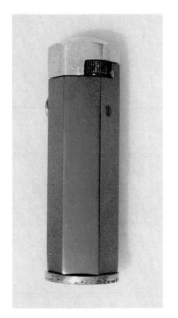

Perma-Wick aluminum lighter
by Haase Mfg. Co. of
Chicago.

Eastern Smelting and
Refining Corp. of Boston Mass.

Sterling Silver Lighters
with Asian Reliefs,
1¹/²" x 2¹/⁴".

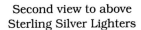

Second view to above
Sterling Silver Lighters

Sterling Silver Lighters.
Right: Marked on bottom "Peruzzie Silver-800 Florence".

Left: 1¹/²" x 2"   Right: 1" x 2"

Different styles of watch lighters.
Most have Swiss movements.

Monroe Lift-Arm lighter, 2" tall.

Pocket lighter with watch insert.

Left: Swiss made lighter with Swank clock.

Right: Marxman Precision Lighter made in Japan with Mastercraft Antimagnetic Swiss made clock.

Both are $1^{1/8}$" x $2^{1/4}$"

Five different styles of musical pocket lighters.

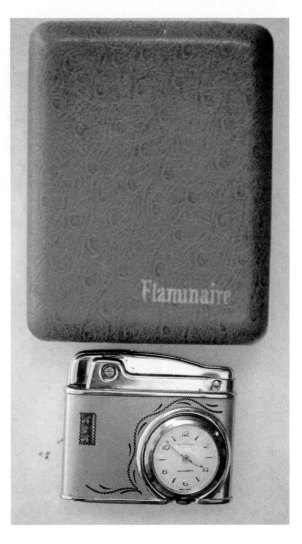

Windson "Flaminaire" Swiss Lighter and Watch.
The watch is Windsor Time, The light is
antimagnetic. Shown with the original case.

Two Royal Musical Lighters.
The red one plays "A Maiden's Prayer".
Both are $1^{1/2}$" x $2^{1/2}$".

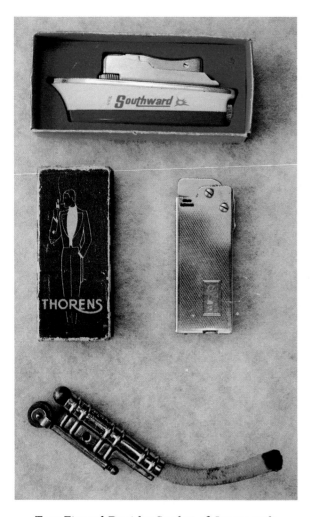

Top: Figural Boat by Sankei of Japan with
original box, 3$^{1/4}$" x 1$^{1/4}$".

Middle: Thorens Lighter with original box, 1" x 2$^{5/8}$".

Bottom: Bowers Army and Navy
lighter, $^{7/8}$" x 4" with wick.

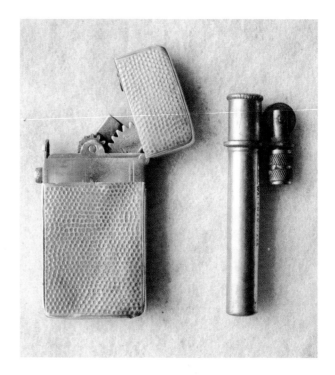

Left: Orlick lighter dated 1911.

Right: WW1 Trench or Hand-made lighter.

Erie Cigar Lighter (wick is missing).
The wick ignited by rolls of caps.

Two Thorens pocket lighters.

Assorted designs of Dunhill pocket lighters,
made in Switzerland, all are 1" x 2$^{1/2}$".

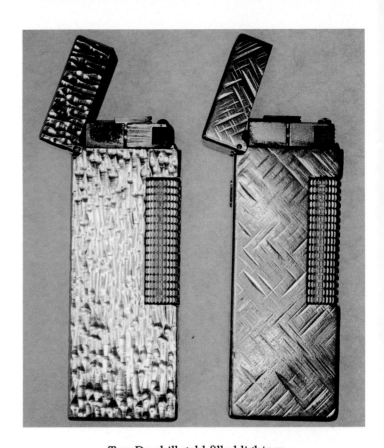

Two Dunhill gold filled lighters,
made in Switzerland, both are 1" x 2$^{1/2}$".

Left: Dunhill – Sterling. Middle: Dunhill – Gold Jacket
Right: Dunhill – Swiss

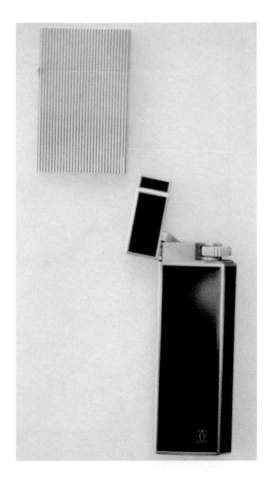

Top: 14K Gold by Tiffany and Co., $^{3/16}$" x 1$^{1/4}$" x 1$^{3/4}$".
Bottom: Cartier butane lighter, $^{1/2}$" x 1" x 2$^{3/4}$".

Two plastic advertising lighters, 1/2" x 2",
both are from Capehart Radios made in Marion, Indiana.

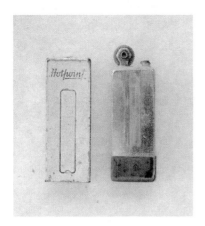

(Front)   (Back)

Weston International Corp. lighter, advertising
"Hotpoint Electric Water Heater," 1/2" x 3/8" x 1 3/4".

Orange bakelite
Art Deco Lighter,
7/8" x 2 3/4".

Striker 1 3/8" x 2 1/4", advertising
"Daniel Burkhartmeier
Cooperage Co., Chicago.

101

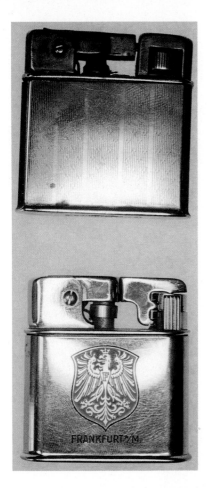

Top: Brass Weltzunder Lighter.

Bottom: "1000 Lunder" D.R.P.
German Lighter, 1³/₄" x ³/₈" x 1³/₄".

Two early Ronson Pocket
Lighters in original boxes.

Top: Evans Trig-A-Lite,
black and red enamel deco 2".
Bottom: Ronson Rondette, 2¹/₄",
Art Metal Works Newark NJ, Pat #19023.

Evans Trig-A-Light, 1¹/₂" x 2".

Golden Arrow brass lighter,
1⁵/₈" x 1⁷/₈" x ¹/₂".

Different styles of Douglass and Clark
Lift-Arm pocket lighters.

#1 Lift-Arm by Ideal, 1¹/₂" x 1³/₄",
#2 Champ-O-Matic from Austria, 1¹/₂" x 2"
#3 Ronson, Canadian Patented 1¹/₂" x 2¹/₄"
#4 Ronson "Standard" England Patented, 1⁵/₈" x 2⁵/₈"
#5 Evans with original box, 1¹/₂" x 2¹/₂"
#6 Evans 1953 "Crossed International Date Line", 1¹/₂" x 2"

Maker Unknown

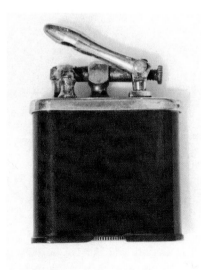

Brass and bakelite Lift-Arm Lighter

Early brass Lift-Arm
pocket lighter by Potter.

Assorted Pocket Lighters.

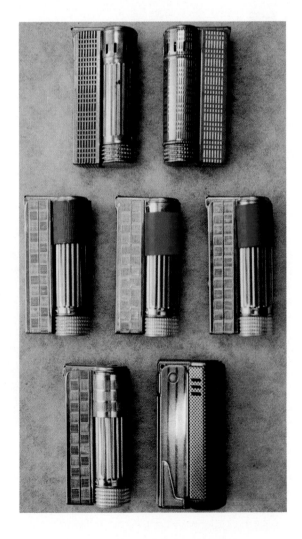

Bottom Right: Imco Gas made in Austria, 1¹/₈" x 2¹/₄".

The first six lighters are all Fortuna,
they each measure 1" x 2³/₈", made in Austria.

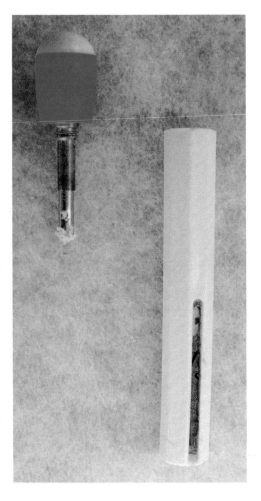

Match striker, plastic, Japan, 4".

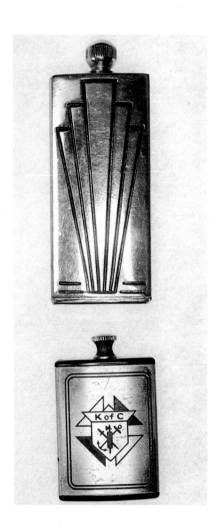

Top: Match King lighter,
Art Deco Chrome, 1" x 2$^{1/4}$".

Bottom: Perma Match Lighter
advertising Knights of Columbus,
Lafayette Council No. 361 KOFC,
1" x 1$^{1/4}$".

Striker advertising
Novitas Sales Co.,
Waitham, MA – 2$^{3/8}$"

Rolls Royce Grill striker 2$^{1/8}$".

Perma Match lighter, 2" x $^{1/8}$" x 1$^{1/4}$"

Top Row:
1994 antique copper, antique brass and
antiuqe silver plated Zippos.

Middle Row:
1994 silver plated Zippo.

Bottom Row:
1994 silver plated Zippo.

All are 1$^{1/2}$" x 2".

1994 Zippo's with litho of playing
cards on the front side. Each Zippo
is in the original box.

All are 1$^{1/2}$" x 2".

Zippo D-Day commemorative tin and lighter set.

Lighter: 1¹/₂" x 2"
Tin: 8¹/₄"

Zippo D-Day commemorative tin and lighter set.

Lighter: 1¹/₂" x 2"
Tin: 4³/₈"

Electric Kool cigarettes penguin, 9".

Store countertop electric advertisement that lights up behind mirrors when it is lit. Clock signed "Brach, Newark N.J.," back signed "Interstate Electric Co. St. Louis, MO." Pat. Model A-1, 11$^{5/8}$" x 10$^{1/2}$".

Fram Filters electric lighter can, 6" x 4$^{1/2}$".

Fram Oil Filters ashtray
5$^{1/2}$" x 4"

Countertop store striker,
maker unknown,
$10^{1/2}$" x $8^{1/2}$".

Red Kamel cigarette store striker,
$3^{1/2}$" x 8" x 9".

Countertop cigar lighter advertising
"Lillian Russels 5¢ Cigars," iron and tin, 11".

Store alcohol burning brass lighter, 4¹/²" x 4".

Iron and brass country store lighter,
10³/⁴" x 5³/⁴".

Trench Art lighter, brass.

Second view of brass Trench lighter

Two Trench Art lighters.
Top: A 1937 half penny on one side.
Bottom: A 1943 half penny on one side, 1" x 1/2".

Trench Art bullet
lighter, brass,
1/2" x 2 3/4", by Nola.

Trench Art bullet lighter,
2 3/4" x 6 1/2", made of brass and copper.

Trench Lighters

Top Left: Holds 1 Cigarette, Souvenir Als Ace,
　　　　　　1918, SGT-HC Carnell, 3" x 1³/⁴".

Top Right: Not Marked, 3" x 2¹/⁴".

Bottom: 3" x 1⁷/⁸".

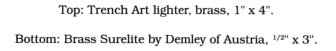

Top: Trench Art lighter, brass, 1" x 4".

Bottom: Brass Surelite by Demley of Austria, ¹/²" x 3".

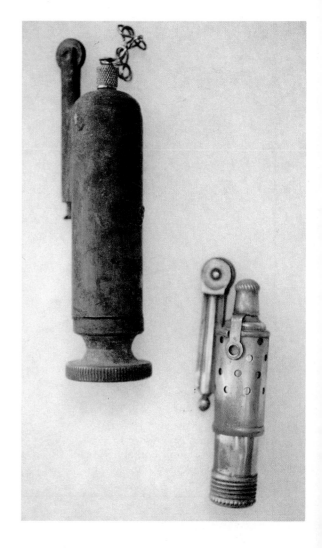

Trench Lighters,
all different styles.

WW1 Trench Lighters, all different styles.
Note: #2 has Russian Insignia.

113

Trench Lighters

Top: 1917, $1^{7/8}$".

Middle Left: Copper and brass, 2".

Middle Right: Basket of flowers, $1^{5/8}$".

Bottom Left: Portrait Je Fais La Guerre,

Eagle with shield on back, 2".

Bottom Right: Silhouette of a man, $1^{1/2}$".

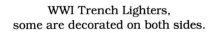

WWI Trench Lighters,
some are decorated on both sides.

Trench Art Lighters, both 1¹/²" x ¹/²".

Trench Art lighters, made of brass, marked "GOT MIT UNS", 1³/⁴", bottom lighter has decorative edge.

WW1 Trench or Hand-made lighter
made from brass shell casings.

Top: Park lighter, brass, 2" x ¹/⁴" x ¹/⁸".
Bottom: Trench Art lighter, 2¹/⁴" x ¹/²" x 1".

WWI Trench Art Lighters
Top: Two Piece Boot lighter.
Left: Lift-Arm lighter.
Bottom: "Book" style lighter.

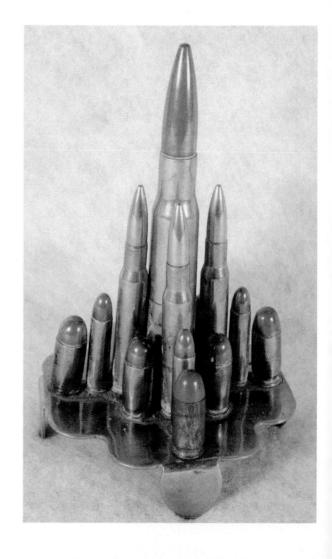

Trench Art Lighter, 16 bullets,
made from copper and brass.
The center bullet is the (6") lighter.

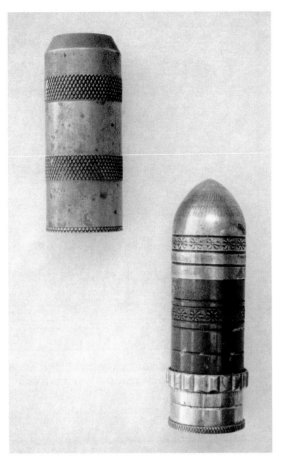

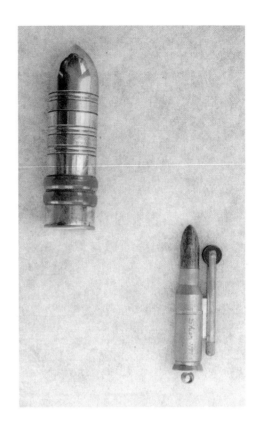

Top: Owin or Nimo, brass,
Trench Art lighter, 1" x 3".

Bottom: Brass Trench Art lighter,
made in France by MER, 1" x 2¹/₄".

Top: Trench Bullet,
made from brass and copper, 3¹/₄" x 1".

Bottom: Japan, Shien 1177, 2¹/₂" .

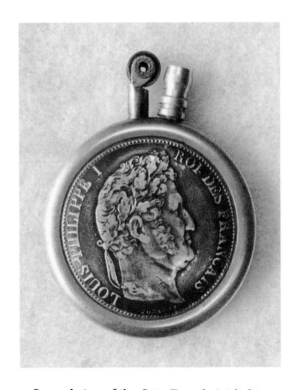

Trench Art lighter with
1847 Coin (*Note:* cap is not original).

Second view of the Coin Trench Art lighter.

Luxor Lighter with emblem
that reads: "Ministere des
Finances" which means
Ministry of Finances, 2³/₄".

Watch made into a lighter, Trench Art style with
emblem on side reading: "Ministere Des Finances"
which means Ministry of Finances, 1³/₄".

Trench Art lighter made
from bullets 3¹/₄".

Ministere Finance brass
construction table lighter,
1¹/₂" x 4³/₄"

Side shot of above
emblem.

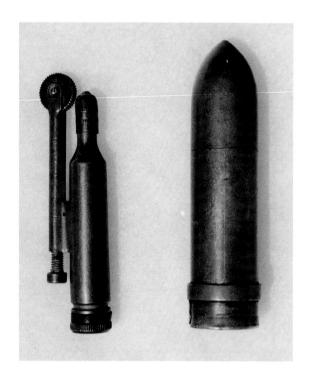

Left: Copper Trench Art.

Right: Bullet Trench Art, by UCR of France.

Trench Art Lighters
Top: Has a 1938 half penny, 1" x 1".
Bottom: Has a Francaise Republique
penny, 1¹/₂" x 2".

Trench type lighter, 2³/₄" x 1¹/₂".

Trench type tabletop,
marked Japan, 3".

Trench type lighter, 2³/₄" x 1¹/₈".

Trench Art lighter and ashtray set.

Lighter: $7^{1/4}$" x $2^{3/16}$"
Ashtray: $2^{5/8}$" x $2^{1/8}$"

Trench Art ashtray and lighter,
6" x $4^{3/4}$".

♪ "Give Zippo for Christmas...one zip and it's lit.
The gift for a lifetime...a sure-fire hit!"

"Zippo lights in a breeze With the greatest of ease!"

(above) ZIPPO TOWN AND COUNTRY. Choice of 6 sparkling designs engraved and inlaid in brilliant ceramic colors. $7.50.

(below) ZIPPO SIGNATURE MODEL. Engraved with signature or message in actual handwriting. Satiny brush finish chrome. $4.

"It's guaranteed mechanically. Repairs are absolutely free!"

(above) ZIPPO ENGINE TURNED. Finely executed design. In bright finish chrome, $5. Sterling silver, $20. 14-karat gold, $175.

(below) ZIPPO LADY BRADFORD TABLE LIGHTER. Luxuriously finished with precious Rhodium, a Platinum group metal. $10.

"Zippo's styled to combine Ruggedness with smart design!"

ZIPPO LEATHER-CRAFTED. Genuine leather cases in red, blue, green and tan. English Morocco and Calfskin. Gold leaf border. $5.50. Personalizing on all Zippo Lighters, only $1.00 extra. See these and other handsome Zippo gift models at your dealer's now ... priced from $3.00 to $175.00*.

"Nothing is so prized As a Zippo personalized!"

"Give Zippo with pleasure— The gift people treasure!"

ZIPPO
one-zip
windproof lighter

© 1951 ZIPPO MFG. CO., BRADFORD, PA.

IN CANADA: Zippo Mfg. Co. Canada Ltd., Niagara Falls, Ont.
*Prices do not include Federal Excise Tax. Prices slightly higher in Canada.

1947 Magazine Ad

121

PALL MALL
FAMOUS CIGARETTES

●THE FIRST TIME you take a Pall Mall in your fingers, you will be impressed by the added distinction the longer size bestows upon this traditionally smart cigarette.

But this added distinction is not its only appealing advantage. For the additional length travels the smoke further, giving you a noticeably cooler and smoother cigarette—thus enhancing the rich flavor of the superb Pall Mall tobaccos.

American Cigarette and Cigar Co.

"WHEREVER PARTICULAR PEOPLE CONGREGA

1940 Magazine Ad

1940's Bakelite ashtray with
match holder advertising Coca-Cola.

1950's Striker Pocket Lighter
advertising Coca-Cola.

1970's Lighter Can
advertising Cocaine.

1960's Lighter Can
advertising Coca-Cola.

1980 Butane lighter by PROF
advertising Coca-Cola.

1962 Cygnus table lighter
advertising Coca-Cola.

1950's Lighter by 3-Lite
advertising Coca-Cola.

1950's Lighter advertising
Coca-Cola by Perma-Pic.

1950's Lighter advertising
Coca-Cola by Rogen-Nesor.

1950's Bakelite Coca-Cola
lighter and pen holder.

Scripto Vu-Lighter
advertising Coca-Cola.

1950's Pull-Apart Lighter.

Dunhill advertising lighter
with a cigarette dispenser,
the base is 3$^{1/2}$" x 8".

Dunhill lighter (opened).

Zippo Pedestal table top
lighter advertising American
Airlines, this is the last
table top lighter that
Zippo made.

Brown and Bigelow Bakelite ashtray
and lighter combo, 5$^{3/4}$" x 3$^{1/4}$".
This piece is advertising Dearborn Tool
and Die Co. in Dearborn, MI.

Brass Lift-Arm advertising
lighters for GMAC PLAN-
Consumer Credit, 3$^{1/4}$" x 2".

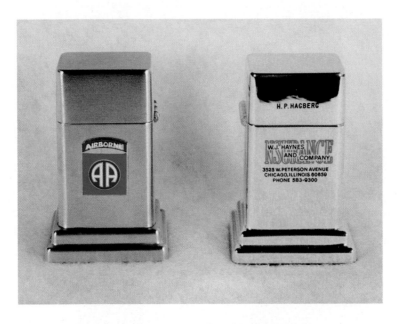

Both are 1950's Barcroft Table Top Lighters,

Left: Advertising Airborne,

Right: Advertising W.J. Haynes and Company.

Zippo table lighter advertising Atlas Energy Group Inc., 2" x 1" x 3¹/₄".

Zippo table lighter advertising the Yellow Pages, 2" x 1" x 3¹/₄".

Zippo table lighter advertising Weaver Brothers Inc. on both sides, 2¹/₈" x 1³/₈" x 3¹/₄".

Dunhill Silent Flame Lighter advertising Logan Clay
Products Co. This item is battery operated, $3^{5/8}$" x $2^{5/8}$".

USA Oil Drum advertising
Dodge Trucks, 3" x $1^{3/4}$".

Both are Idealine Table Lighters,
Left-Advertising Albee Homes,
Right-Advertising Panama Pacific Exposition
in San Francisco, $2^{3/8}$" x $2^{5/6}$".

Hong Kong Perma Match
Lighter, $1^{1/2}$" x 1" x $3/8$".

Barlow lighter advertising
Strato-Track Inc. This item was made
in Japan, 1" x $3/4$" x $4^{1/4}$", base 2" x $1^{1/2}$".

Left: Ceramic lighter advertising Henry McKenna
Hand Made Whiskey made in Japan,

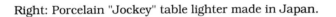

Right: Porcelain "Jockey" table lighter made in Japan.

Apricot Liqueur by DeKuyper Bottle
made into a lighter with the tax
sticker on it for $3^{1/8}$¢, $1^{1/4}$" x $4^{1/2}$".

Detroit Michigan Canners Coca-Cola
Can manufactured under license
granted to Elgin Scientific Glass
Co. Inc. in Elgin, IL., $5^{1/2}$" x $2^{5/8}$".

Beer Cans with Japan lighters on the inside, $5^{3/4}$" x $2^{5/8}$".

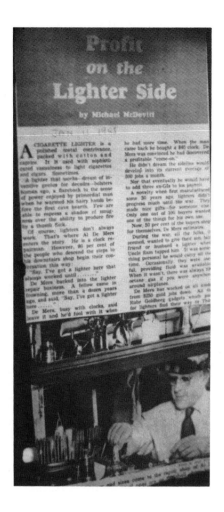

This photo is associated with the photo of the Crosley
Station Wagon. This lighter went on top and lit up
when the brakes were used. One of a kind, 14³/₄".

Demers Store located in Coloumbus, Ohio is still in business.

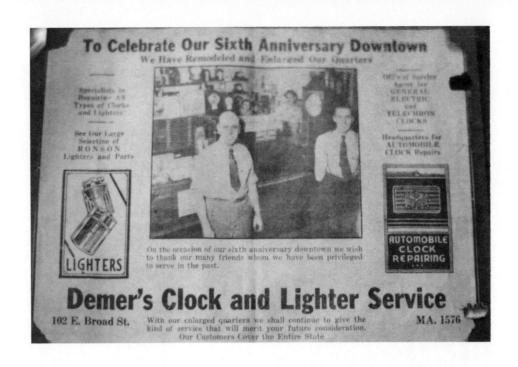

clock, flap position indicator, gyropilot pressure gauges and instrument vacuum gauge. At the navigator's station are a seven-foot chart table, cabinet and instruments. There is an overhead turret for celestial observations and two drift sight stations under the wings. Opposite the navigator sits the radio operator, with three transmitters, three receivers and the radio direction finder. Just back of him is the flight engineer, responsible for the power plants and the calculation of power and fuel required for the flight. Facing the engineer is a panel carrying twenty-six instruments—tachometers, fuel quantity and flow indicators, oil temperature and pressure dials, air-fuel ratio indicators, a potentiometer showing temperature at two cylinder heads and cylinder bases of each engine; and, among others, an indicator which would detect presence of carbon monoxide in the heating system and shut it off automatically. In addition, the engineer has individual engine and propeller controls, mixtures and pressure regulators and hand-operated emergency fuel pumps. One dial shows up water in the fuel tanks, and there is a power-operated fire extinguishing system. An important safety factor is easy access to every motor during flight. Final authority is the master, who sits behind the navigator, correlating the crew's functions and directing the flight.

Lifelike Radio Robot Speaks, Walks and Lights Cigarette

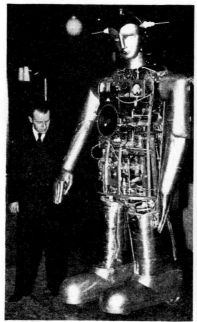

© Planet News, Ltd.
Left, "Sabor's" jacket is removed to show the complexity of its mechanism. Right, the robot lighting a cigarette for its inventor

After ten years of work, a Swiss inventor has completed a lifelike robot seven feet tall and weighing 400 pounds. Controlled by radio, "Sabor," as the robot is christened, walks forward, backward or sidewise, and forms words correctly with its lips in speaking. The mechanical man will answer questions and can light its master's cigar.

Article from a 1939 magazine.

Lights the Smokes . . . of the Nation . . . .

U.S. PAT. RE. NO. 19023 TRADE MARK REGISTERED

RONSON

CANADIAN PAT. NOS. 288,148—289,889 308,844—311,040 BRITISH PAT. NO. 291,695

WORLD'S GREATEST LIGHTER

FLIP—It's lit! RELEASE—It's out!   One Finger, One Motion

Lighter—Cigarette Case Combinations

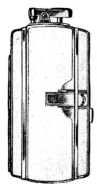

Ronson Sportcase. Genuine chromium plated, engine turned and richly enameled in tortoise. Polished monogram shield.
No. 83J313.

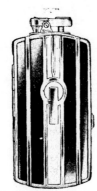

Ronson Sportcase. Genuine chromium plated and richly enameled in black and white. Polished monogram shield.
No. 83J314.

RONSON
SMART SET

A new RONSON lighter case combination holding 12 cigarettes. Compactly built, takes up very little room. Large fuel capacity.

Illustrated to right.

Ronson Smart Set. Chromium plated, engine turned and richly enameled in tortoise and ivory.
No. 83J239.

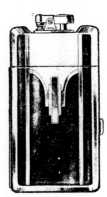

Ronson Mastercase. Chromium plated and richly enameled in black. Raised monogram shield.
No. 83J45.

Ronson Mastercase. Genuine chromium plated, engine turned and richly enameled in black and white. Polished monogram shield.
No. 83J315.

RONSON
MASTERCASE

½ ACTUAL SIZE SHOWN

Ronson Mastercase. In Dureum (a through-and-through alloy in rich yellow gold effect). Engine turned and richly enameled in tortoise and ivory. Polished monogram shield.
No. 83J316.

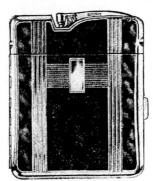

Ronson Ten-A-Case. Genuine chromium plated, engine turned and richly enameled in two-tone tortoise. Polished monogram shield.
No. 83J317.

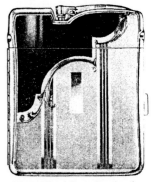

Ronson Ten-A-Case. Genuine chromium plated, engine turned and hand engraved. Richly enameled in black. Polished monogram shield.
No. 83J318.

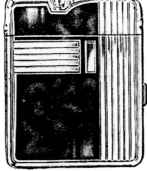

Ronson Ten-A-Case. In Dureum (a through-and-through alloy in rich yellow gold effect). Engine turned and richly enameled in tortoise. Polished monogram shield.
No. 83J319.

Ronson Monarch. Engine turned and richly enameled in black. Polished monogram shield.
No. 83J358.

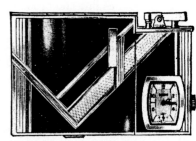

Ronson Kingcase with Watch. Lighter cigarette case combination with reliable built-in stem-wind and stem-set watch. Genuine chromium plated, engine turned and richly enameled in black. Polished monogram shield.

RONSON *Kingcase* No. 83J247.

1938-1939 Catalog Page

132

Lights the Smokes ... **of the Nation** ...

U.S. PAT. RE.
NO. 19023
TRADE MARK
REGISTERED

RONSON

CANADIAN PAT. NOS.
308,148—309,889
308,844—311,040
BRITISH PAT.
NO. 291,695

WORLD'S GREATEST LIGHTER

FLIP—It's lit! RELEASE—It's out!

One Finger, One Motion

POCKET LIGHTERS

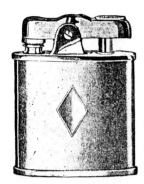

Ronson Princess. Chromium plated.
Polished shield.
No. 83J26.   Princess.
No. 83J27.   Standard.

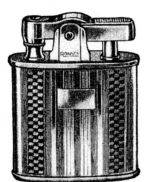

Ronson Princess. Genuine Chromium
plated in fancy design. Polished monogram shield.
No. 83J301.   Princess.
No. 83J302.   Standard.

**Shown
Actual
Size**

Ronson Princess. Chromium plated,
richly enameled in Black with polished
monogram shield.
No. 83J228.   Princess.
No. 83J229.   Standard.

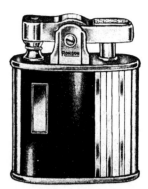

Ronson Princess. Chromium plated
and enameled in Black and White.
Polished monogram shield.
No. 83J303.   Princess.

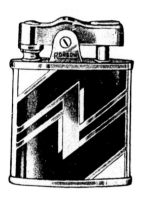

Ronson Princess. Chromium and
richly enameled in Tortoise and Ivory.
Polished monogram shield.
No. 83J230.

Ronson Princess. Chromium plated,
"Engine Turned" and enameled in
Black. Monogram shield.
No. 83J304.   Princess.

Ronson Princess. In Dureum (a
through and through alloy in rich
yellow gold effect). "Engine-Turned"
with polished monogram shield.
No. 83J232.   Princess.
No. 83J305.   Standard.

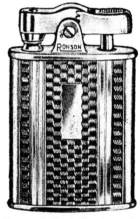

Ronson Banker. Chromium plated
"Engine-Turned." Monogram shield.
Large fuel capacity.
No. 83J231.

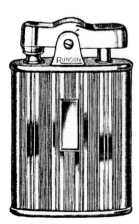

Ronson Banker. In Dureum
(a through alloy in gold effect). "Engine-Turned" with
monogram shield.
No. 83J306.

Ronson Gem. Genuine chro-
mium plated. "Engine-Turned"
and richly enameled in Black.
Polished monogram shield.
No. 83J307.

Ronson Gem. Genuine
chromium plated. "Engine-
Turned" and richly enameled
in White. Polished monogram
shield.
No. 83J308.

Ronson Gem. Genuine
chromium plated. "Engine-
Turned" and richly enameled
in Black and White. Polished
monogram shield.
No. 83J309.

Ronson Gem. In Dureum
(a through and through alloy
in rich yellow gold effect).
"Engine-Turned" and hand
engraved. Richly enameled in
Tortoise. Polished monogram
shield.
No. 83J310.

1938-1939 Catalog Page

Lights the Smokes ... of the Nation....

U. S. PAT. RE.
NO. 19023
TRADE MARK
REGISTERED

RONSON

CANADIAN PAT. NOS.
288,148—289,889
308,844—311,040
BRITISH PAT.
NO. 291,695

FLIP—It's lit! RELEASE—It's out!

WORLD'S GREATEST LIGHTER

One Finger, One Motion

RONSON TOUCH-TIP WITH CALENDAR PAD

Touch-Tip and Watch Combination

Ronson Touch Tip and Eight Day Clock Combination

Ronson Touch-Tip with Calendar Pad. Lighter is a modern version of the famous Ronson Touch-Tip with its liberal fuel capacity. The replaceable appointment calendar is fastened under an attractive gold stamped hinged cover. The daily calendar pages themselves provide space for half-hour appointments throughout the day, with additional room for memoranda and calendar for the current and following months. Perforated lines permit the removal of the date panel for incomplete memos. or the entire page.

A convenient pencil or pen ledge is fastened between Touch-Tip and Pad. Attractive duo-bronze finish, enameled in tortoise.

No. 83J359.

Ronson Touch-Tip and Watch Combination. Enameled in Tortoise or Black with base and fitments in polished Chromium Plate. Built-in watch—dependable stem-wound, stem-set. Height 4 inches.

No. 83J197.

Shown in greatly reduced size

Ronson Touch-Tip & Eight-Day Clock Combination. A handsome, ample and substantial desk or table combination, featuring modern-classic lines. Clock has a highly dependable 8-day movement and a large, legible, rectangular dial; the Touch-Tip Lighter has a large fuel capacity, requiring filling only once in several months. The model is finished in Copper-Bronze, in two-tone effect, while dial is finished in Two-Tone Silver with black numerals. Height 5 inches, Width 3 1/8 inches, Length 7 inches.

No. 83J288.

Shown about half actual size

Ronson Roll Top Touch-Tip Cigarette Cabinet

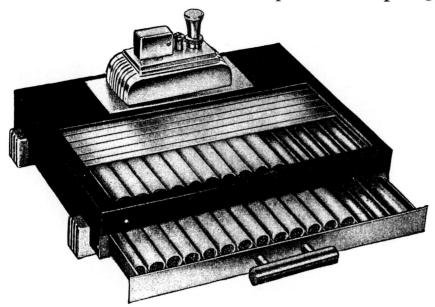

Ronson Roll-Top Touch-Tip Cigarette Cabinet. Streamlined Touch-Tip Lighter built into handsome, ingenious Cigarette Cabinet. As the drawer is pulled open, the metal slatted top slides back mysteriously. Both the upper compartments and the drawer space are fluted to hold cigarettes in place. Exterior handsomely plated in genuine Chromium and richly enameled in Black. Interior of compartment and drawer fashioned in RONSON Dureum, a thru-and-thru alloy in rich yellow gold effect. Height 3 3/8 inches, Width 6 1/4 inches, Length 8 inches.

No. 83J289.

1938-1939 Catalog Page

Evans Combination Cigarette Case with Lighter. Knife edge model, non-tarnishing chromium finish, hammered design with inlaid black French enamel.
No. 83J192.

Evans Combination Cigarette Case with Lighter. Non-tarnishing chromium finish. French enamel front. Colors: Black, Blue, Green or Red.
No. 83J193.

Evans Combination Cigarette Case with Lighter. Non-tarnishing chromium finish with French enamel front. Colors: Black, Blue, Green or Red.
No. 83J277.

Evans Combination Cigarette Case with Lighter. Non-tarnishing chromium finish. French enamel front. Enamel colors: Black, Red, Green or Blue.
No. 83J76.

Evans Combination Cigarette Case with Lighter. New style, non-tarnishing chromium finish. French black enamel front and back.
No. 83J114.

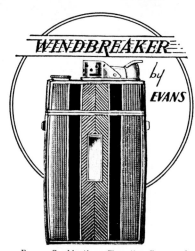

WINDBREAKER by *EVANS*

Evans Combination Cigarette Case and Lighter with windshield. Non-tarnishing chromium finish; engine-turned design with Black French enamel.
No. 83J362.

Evans Combination Cigarette Case and Lighter with double vanity. Non-tarnishing chromium finish with Black French enamel front and back with genuine hand-painted straw colored Cloisonne vanity cover. Fitted with large mirror, loose powder container and rouge.
No. 83J280.

Evans "20-Pak" Combinations

Evans Combination Cigarette Case and Lighter. Non-tarnishing chromium finish with Black French enamel front and back. Holds fifteen cigarettes.
No. 83J82.
As above: Without shield and finished in simulated burl maple French enamel.
No. 83J83.

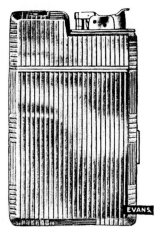

Evans "20-Pak" Combination Cigarette Case and Lighter. Non-tarnishing chromium finish; engine-turned design. Holds full pack.
No. 83J299. Chromium.
As above: French enameled front and chromium trim. Colors: Black, Burgundy, Green, Navy and White.
No. 83J300. Enameled.

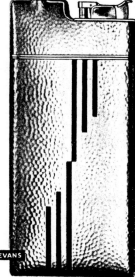

Evans Combination Cigarette Case and Lighter. Chromium finish. Thin knife edge model; holds fifteen cigarettes. Inlaid Black French enamel stripes.
No. 83J81.

Lights the Smokes ... of the Nation....

U.S. PAT. RE.
NO. 19023
TRADE MARK
REGISTERED

RONSON

CANADIAN PAT. NOS.
288,148 — 289,889
308,844 — 311,040
BRITISH PAT.
NO. 291,695

FLIP—*It's lit!* RELEASE—*It's out!*   WORLD'S GREATEST LIGHTER   One Finger, One Motion

POCKET LIGHTERS

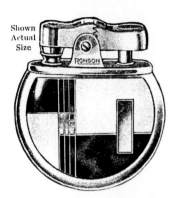

Shown Actual Size

Ronson Rondette. Genuine chromium plated. Engine turned and richly enameled in black and white. Polished monogram shield.

No. 83J311.

Ronson Rondette. Genuine chromium plated, engine turned and richly enameled in black. Polished monogram shield.

No. 83J312.

Ronson Viceroy. Genuine chromium plated, engine turned and richly enameled in tortoise. Polished monogram shield.

No. 83J353.

Ronson Jeweled Coronet. In dureum (a through-and-through alloy in rich yellow gold effect). Richly enameled in black.

No. 83J354.

Ronson Heart. Chromium plated. Engine turned and richly enameled in black with polished monogram shield.

No. 83J234.

RONSON PENCILITER

PRESS — and it's lit!

Ronson Penciliter. A genuine Ronson Lighter incorporated in a superfine propel-repel pencil. Large fuel capacity, good for pipes as well as cigarettes and cigars. Extra leads and eraser. Polished chrome with engine turned design, pocket clip **and** monogram shield. Pearled green or black writing grip. The lighter takes no extra room, the pencil costs no extra money.

No. 83J43.

In reduced size.)

RONSON TWO-PIECE SET

Ronson Set. Cigarette Case and Princess Thin Model Automatic Lighter. Chromium plated, rich black or burgundy enamel. Cigarette case holds 10 cigarettes. Each set attractively boxed.

No. 83J109.

RONSON

ACCESSORIES

INSURE

STORE

TRAFFIC

FOR

YOU!

This Package Contains
3 GENUINE **RONSON** FLINTS
Extra Length   Super Quality
For Best Service In
RONSON WORLD'S GREATEST LIGHTER
U. S. PAT. Re. No. 19023
INSIST ON GENUINE RONSON FLINTS
FLIP—*it's lit!*
RELEASE—*it's out!*

For best results, Ronson owners should use only genuine Ronson Flints. Size, shape and quality insure best results in Ronson and all other lighters. Three in package.

No. 83J44.

To Keep Your RONSON Lighter Fit
Use This
RONSON SERVICE KIT
WORLD'S GREATEST LIGHTER
CONTAINS:
PACKAGE OF IGNITERS   FUEL-FILL CAPSULE
SPARK WHEEL BRUSH   WICK AND INSERTER
INSTRUCTION BOOKLET

Ronson Service Kit. Metal box contains three Ronson Flints, Wick and Inserter. Fuel-Fill Capsule. Spark-Wheel cleaning brush and instruction booklet. Retails at 25c.

Dealer display carton holds one dozen Ronson Service Kits.

No. 83J329.

1938-1939 Catalog Page

VANITY SMOKING COMBINATIONS

RONSON *Literpact*

Case Shown Open
Illustrations shown less than actual size.

Ronson Literpact. A handsome compact containing loose powder with sifter and puff, as well as mirror. Includes a genuine Ronson Lighter, built into compact. The whole ensemble takes no more room than the usual compact, but thanks to a fuel chamber cleverly concealed in its outside edge, the attractive little case does double duty, as a lighter as well as a powder box.

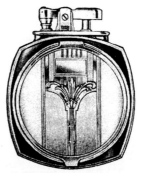

Ronson Literpact. Genuine chromium plated, "Engine-Turned" and hand engraved. Richly enameled in Black and White. Polished monogram shield.
No. 83J321.

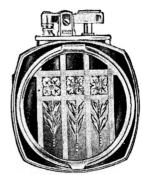

Ronson Literpact. In Dureum (a through and through alloy in rich yellow gold effect). "Engine-Turned" and hand engraved. Richly enameled in Tortoise.
No. 83J322.

RONSON TOUCH-TIPS and TOUCH-TIP COMBINATIONS

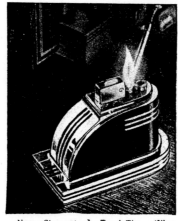

RONSON Touch-Tip and Cigarette Humidor or Box

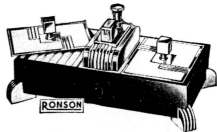

Ronson Touch-Tip and Cigarette Humidors. Streamlined chromium plated Touch-Tip set between two cedar-lined cigarette boxes, richly enameled in Black and White. Height 3⅝ inches, width 4½ inches, length 8 inches.
No. 83J249.

Ronson Touch-Tip. (Illustrated at Left.) Fitments and base of polished chrome, all metal body finished in Black, Tortoise or White enamel. Polished center shield.
No. 83J106.

New Streamlined Touch-Tip. (Illustrated at right.) Featuring speedy flow lines of crack modern railway trains. Chromium plated and richly enameled in Black.
No. 83J236.
Gold and Tortoise
No. 83J237.

RONSON Touch-Tip with Cigarette Dispenser

RONSON Touch-Tip and Ash-Tray

Ronson Touch-Tip and Ash Tray Set. Modern chromium plated Touch-Tip mounted on richly enameled Tortoise chromium trimmed base which also contains an ash receiver. Height 3½ inches, width 4 inches, length 7⅛ inches.
No. 83J330.

RONSON Touch-Tip and Humidor

Ronson Touch-Tip Smoking Set. (Illustrated at Right.) Streamlined Touch-Tip attached to oval-shaped Cigarette Box, which holds a liberal supply of cigarettes. Fashioned in Dureum (a solid through and through alloy in rich yellow-gold effect) and richly enameled in Tortoise. Height 3¾ inches, width 3¼ inches, length 5¼ inches.
No. 83J331.

Touch-Tip Cigarette Dispenser. Touch-Tip and cigarette box with automatic delivery system, plated in polished chrome, richly enameled in Black and decorated with relief bands. Base finished in gunmetal, with polished chromium plated corner rests (felt padded). Height 4½ inches, width 4⅝ inches, depth 7¾ inches.
No. 83J196.

1938-1939 Catalog Page

Lights the Smokes ... of the Nation ...

RONSON

U. S. PAT. RE. NO. 19.023 TRADE MARK REGISTERED

CANADIAN PAT. NOS. 288,148—289,889 308,844—311,040 BRITISH PAT. NO. 291,695

WORLD'S GREATEST LIGHTER

FLIP—It's lit! RELEASE—It's out!

One Finger, One Motion

LIGHTER CIGARETTE CASE COMBINATIONS

Ronson Supercase. Genuine chromium plated, "Engine-Turned" in fluted effect and richly enameled in Black. Polished monogram shield.
No. 83J328.

RONSON
SUPERCASE

Shown ½
Actual Size

RONSON Magnacase

RONSON
MAGNACASE

Ronson Magnacase. Chromium plated. Two-tone Tortoise enamel. With shield. Holds 15 cigarettes on a line.
No. 83J112.

Ronson Twentycase. Genuine chromium plated "Heavy Engine-Turning" and richly enameled in Black. Polished monogram shield.
No. 83J326.

Ronson Tuxedo. Genuine chromium plated. "Engine-Turned" and richly enameled in Black. Polished monogram shield.
No. 83J320.

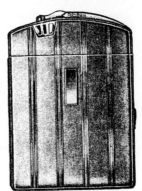

Ronson Twentycase. Chromium plated, "Engine-Turned." Polished monogram shield.
No. 83J245.

Ronson Twentycase. In Dureum (a through and through alloy in rich yellow gold effect). "Engine-Turned" and richly enameled in Tortoise. Polished monogram shield.
No. 83J327.

RONSON
Beauticase

RONSON
TUXEDO

Ronson Beauticase. In Dureum (a through and through alloy in rich yellow gold effect). "Engine-Turned" and richly enameled in Tortoise.
No. 83J242.

RONSON VANITY Smoking Combinations

Indispensable Aids to Milady

RONSON
MASTERPACT

Masterpact. Genuine chromium plated, "Engine-Turned" and richly enameled in Tortoise and Turquoise. Polished monogram shield.
No. 83J323.

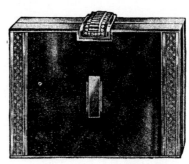

RONSON
Kitcase

Ronson Jeweled Kitcase. A handsome vanity case containing milady's every toilet and smoking necessity for daytime and formal use. A cigarette compartment, concealed lighter, powder compartment with sifter and puff, polished chromium mirror and moire envelope containing comb, with ample space for lipstick and "mad money." Lighter swings out when wanted. Case closes with stunning jewel-clasp. Genuine chromium plated. "Engine-Turned" and richly enameled in Black. Polished monogram shield.
No. 83J324.

1938-1939 Catalog Page

WINDBREAKER *by* **EVANS**

Evans Automatic Lighter. Non-tarnishing chromium finish Barley-corn, engine turned and modern striped design.
No. 83J365

Evans Windbreaker Automatic Lighter with Windshield. Non-tarnishing chromium finish engine turned design with black French enamel stripes.
No. 83J361

Evans Automatic Lighter. Non-tarnishing, chromium finish with attractive barley-corn design. Polished center shield and sides. Illustration actual size.
No. 83J131

Evans Automatic Lighter. Petite style in a non-tarnishing highly polished Chromium finish. Striped design.
No. 83J176

Evans Automatic Lighter. Non-tarnishing chromium finish barley-corn engine-turned design.
No. 83J182

Evans Automatic Lighter. Non-tarnishing chromium finish barley-corn engine-turned design with stripes and shield.
No. 83J256

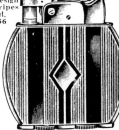

Evans Automatic Lighter. Chromium finish, knife edge. Black enamel design.
No. 83J167

Evans Automatic Lighter. Non-tarnishing chromium finish, modern decoration and barley-corn engine-turned design.
No. 83J257

Evans Automatic Lighter. Newest non-tarnishing Gilt finish. Attractive barley-corn design.
No. 83J177

Evans Automatic Lighter. Newest non-tarnishing Gilt finish. Modern barley-corn design.
No. 83J178

Evans Automatic Lighter. Non-tarnishing chromium finish, French enamel front and back. Enamel color: Black.
No. 83J183

Evans Automatic Lighter. Non-tarnishing chromium finish. French enamel front and back. Enameled color: Black.
No. 83J186

Evans Automatic Lighter. Non-tarnishing Chromium finish. Black Enameled front and back.
No. 83J283

Evans Dice Lighter. Assorted colored genuine catalin bases with contrasting spots. Evans automatic lighter unit.
No. 83J194.

WORLD'S LARGEST MANUFACTURERS OF STYLE ACCESSORIES

1938-1939 Catalog Page

Index for
Brands and Manufacturers

Index for
Type of Lighters

Price Guide

Page 5
Top Left .... 75.00+
Top Right .... 650.00+
Bottom Left .... 400.00+
Bottom Right .... 250.00+

Page 6
Lighter .... 750.00+

Page 7
Top Left .... 40.00+
Top Right .... 40.00+
Bottom .... 60.00+

Page 8
Top Left (each) .... 3.00+
Top Right Picture
     top .... 40.00+
     bottom .... 50.00+
Bottom (each) .... 3.00+

Page 9
Top .... 20.00+
Bottom Picture
     top .... 3.00+
     bottom .... 15.00+

Page 10
Top Left .... 75.00+
Top Right .... 300.00+
Bottom Left .... 75.00+
Bottom Right .... 25.00+

Page 11
Top Left .... 40.00+
Top Right .... 40.00+
Bottom Left .... 65.00+
Bottom Right .... 50.00+

Page 12
Top Left Picture
     each .... 10.00+
     full card .... 140.00+
Top Right (case only) .... 100.00+
Bottom Picture
     top .... 90.00+
     bottom .... 100.00+

Page 13
Top Left .... 300.00+
Top Right .... 175.00+
Bottom Left .... 200.00+
Bottom Right .... 150.00+

Page 14
Top .... 300.00+
Bottom Left .... 900.00+
Bottom Right .... 300.00+

Page 15
Top .... 850.00+
Bottom .... 1,400.00+

Page 16
Top Left .... 175.00+
Top Right .... 150.00+
Bottom Left .... 35.00+
Bottom Right .... 50.00+

Page 17
Top Left .... 400.00+
Top Right .... 150.00+
Bottom Left .... 175.00+
Bottom Right .... 175.00+

Page 18
Top Left .... 250.00+
Top Right .... 150.00+
Bottom Left .... 250.00+
Bottom Right .... 150.00+

Page 19
Left .... 500.00+
Top Right .... 350.00+
Bottom Right .... 400.00+

Page 20
Top Left .... 150.00+
Top Right .... 150.00+
Bottom Left .... 150.00+
Bottom Right .... 125.00+

Page 21
Top Left .... 325.00+
Top Right .... 450.00+
Bottom .... 250.00+

Page 22
Top Left .... 100.00+
Top Right .... 250.00+
Bottom Left .... 160.00+
Bottom Right .... 225.00+

Page 23
Left .... 500.00+
Top Right .... 65.00+
Bottom Right .... 40.00+

Page 24
Top Left .... 35.00+
Top Right .... 45.00+
Bottom Left .... 68.00+

Page 25
Top Left .... 25.00+
Top Right .... 15.00+
Bottom Left (each) .... 2.00+
Bottom Right .... 5.00+

Page 26
Top Left (each) .... 5.00+
Top Right .... 15.00+
Bottom Left .... 25.00+
Bottom Right (each) .... 5.00+

Page 27
Top Left Picture
     top left .... 5.00+
     top right .... 7.00+
     bottom .... 10.00+
Top Right (each) .... 10.00+
Bottom Left (each) .... 5.00+
Bottom Right (each) .... 5.00+

Page 28
Top Left .... 60.00+
Right .... 20.00+
Bottom Left .... 200.00+

Page 29
Top Picture
     top .... 8.00+
     botttom .... 11.00+
Bottom (each) .... 30.00+

Page 30
Firefly .... 200.00+

Page 31
Top Left Picture
     top .... 40.00+
     bottom .... 20.00+
Top Right .... 85.00+
Bottom .... 50.00+

Page 32
Top Left .... 100.00+
Top Right .... 75.00+
Bottom Left .... 100.00+
Bottom Right Picture
     top left .... 40.00+
     top right .... 50.00+
     bottom .... 50.00+

Page 33
Top Left .... 100.00+
Top Right .... 90.00+
Bottom Left .... 100.00+
Bottom Right .... 110.00+

Page 34
Top Left (each) .... 30.00+
Top Right .... 75.00+
Bottom Left .... 125.00+
Bottom Right .... 90.00+

Page 35
Top Left .... 15.00+
Top Right .... 7.00+

Middle Right .... 15.00+
Bottom Left .... 50.00+
BottomRight .... 35.00+

Page 36
Top Left .... 10.00+
Top Right .... 50.00+
Bottom Left Picture
    left .... 30.00+
    right .... 7.00+
Bottom Right (each) .... 20.00+

Page 37
Top .... 75.00+
Bottom Left .... 20.00+
Bottom Middle .... 15.00+
Bottom Right .... 50.00+

Page 38
Ronson Figure .... 900.00+

Page 39
Top Left .... 35.00+
Top Right .... 35.00+
Bottom Left .... 25.00+
Bottom Right .... 35.00+

Page 40
Top Left .... 50.00+
Top Right .... 20.00+
Bottom Left .... 35.00+
Bottom Right .... 25.00+

Page 41
Top Left (set) .... 30.00+
Top Right .... 10.00+
Middle Right .... 35.00+
Bottom Left .... 35.00+
Bottom Right .... 40.00+

Page 42
Top Left .... 75.00+
Top Right .... 20.00+
Bottom Left .... 50.00+
Bottom Right .... 50.00+

Page 43
Top Left .... 30.00+
Top Right .... 25.00+
Bottom Left .... 18.00+
Bottom Right .... 40.00+

Page 44
Top Left .... 45.00+
Top Right (each) .... 35.00+
Bottom Left .... 60.00+
Middle Right .... 65.00+
Bottom Right .... 30.00+

Page 45
Top Left .... 400.00+
Top Right .... 40.00+
Bottom Left .... 125.00+
Bottom Right .... 50.00+

Page 46
Top Left .... 20.00+
Top Right (each) .... 7.00+
Middle Left .... 25.00+
Bottom Left .... 35.00+
Bottom Right .... 35.00+

Page 47
Top .... 1,000.00+
Bottom .... 50.00+

Page 48
Top .... 60.00+
Bottom Left .... 10.00+
Bottom Right .... 70.00+

Page 49
Top Left Picture
    left .... 10.00+
    right .... 5.00+
Top Right .... 12.00+
Middle Left .... 30.00+
Middle Right .... 7.00+
Bottom .... 35.00+

Page 50
Top .... 50.00+
Middle Left .... 35.00+
Middle Right .... 40.00+
Bottom (each) .... 25.00+

Page 51
Top Left .... 40.00+
Bottom Left .... 300.00+
Right .... 25.00+

Page 52
Top Left .... 65.00+
Top Right .... 65.00+
Bottom Left .... 35.00+
Bottom Right .... 40.00+

Page 53
Top Left .... 75.00+
Top Right .... 110.00+
Bottom Left .... 60.00+
Bottom Right .... 45.00+

Page 54
Top Left .... 60.00+
Top Right .... 35.00+
Bottom Left .... 45.00+
Bottom Right .... 50.00+

Page 55
Top Left .... 60.00+
Top Right .... 60.00+
Bottom .... 75.00+

Page 56
Top Left .... 35.00+
Top Right .... 30.00+
Bottom Left .... 40.00+
Bottom Right .... 35.00+

Page 57
Top Left .... 400.00+
Right .... 200.00+
Bottom Left .... 150.00+

Page 58
Top Left .... 65.00+
Top Right .... 50.00+
Bottom Left .... 30.00+
Bottom Right .... 40.00+

Page 59
Top Left .... 55.00+
Top Right .... 90.00+
Middle Left .... 275.00+
Middle Right .... 40.00+
Bottom .... 40.00+

Page 60
Top Left .... 65.00+
Top Right .... 85.00+
Bottom Left .... 40.00+
Bottom Right .... 30.00+

Page 61
Top Left .... 90.00+
Top Right .... 150.00+
Bottom Left .... 45.00+
Bottom Right .... 30.00+

Page 62
Top Left (each) .... 5.00+
Top Right .... 20.00+
Middle Right .... 75.00+
Bottom Left .... 15.00+
Bottom Middle .... 50.00+
Bottom Right .... 45.00+

Page 63
Top Left (each) .... 30.00+
Top Right .... 65.00+
Bottom Left .... 35.00+
Bottom Right .... 40.00+

Page 64
Top Left .... 25.00+
Top Right .... 25.00+
Bottom Picture
    left .... 50.00+
    right .... 30.00+

Page 65
Left .... 40.00+
Top Right .... 20.00+
Bottom Right .... 35.00+

Page 66
Top Left .... 225.00+
Bottom Left .... 90.00+
Right .... 50.00+

Page 67
Top Left .... 125.00+
Top Right .... 100.00+
Bottom Left .... 100.00+
Bottom Right .... 250.00+

Page 68

Top Left .... 250.00+
Top Right .... 450.00+
Bottom Left .... 75.00+
Bottom Right (each) .... 75.00+

Page 69

Top Left .... 175.00+
Top Right .... 65.00+
Bottom Left .... 75.00+
Bottom Right .... 150.00+

Page 70

Top Left .... 75.00+
Top Right .... 250.00+
Bottom Left .... 75.00+
Bottom Right (each) .... 95.00+

Page 71

Top Left .... 200.00+
Top Right .... 125.00+
Middle Left .... 125.00+
Middle Right .... 75.00+
Bottom .... 85.00+

Page 72

Top .... 40.00+
Bottom Left .... 50.00+
Bottom Middle .... 50.00+
Bottom Right .... 225.00+

Page 73

Top Left .... 85.00+
Top Right .... 200.00+
Middle Left .... 60.00+
Bottom Left (set) .... 85.00+
Bottom Right .... 60.00+

Page 74

Top Left .... 75.00+
Top Right .... 60.00+
Bottom Left .... 175.00+
Bottom Right .... 140.00+

Page 75

Top Left .... 225.00+
Top Right .... 200.00+
Middle left .... 75.00+
Bottom Right .... 140.00+

Page 76

Top Left .... 75.00+
Top Right .... 175.00+
Bottom Left .... 75.00+
Bottom Right .... 75.00+

Page 77

Top Left .... 125.00+
Top Right .... 85.00+
Middle Left .... 75.00+
Middle Right .... 150.00+
Bottom .... 100.00+

Page 78

Top Left .... 75.00+

Top Right .... 50.00+
Middle Left .... 90.00+
Middle Right .... 50.00+
Bottom .... 150.00+

Page 79

Top Left .... 100.00+
Top Right .... 75.00+
Bottom Left .... 75.00+
Bottom Right .... 100.00+

Page 80

Top Left .... 200.00+
Top Right .... 175.00+
Middle Left .... 200.00+
Bottom Left .... 90.00+
Bottom Right .... 100.00+

Page 81

Top Left .... 90.00+
Top Right .... 200.00+
Bottom Left .... 250.00+
Bottom Right .... 250.00+

Page 82

Top Left .... 125.00+
Top Right .... 225.00+
Bottom Right .... 225.00+
Bottom Left .... 300.00+

Page 83

Top Left .... 125.00+
Top Right .... 60.00+
Bottom Left .... 125.00+
Bottom Right .... 90.00+

Page 84

Top Left .... 150.00+
Top Right .... 50.00+
Bottom Left Picture
    top .... 60.00+
    bottom .... 30.00+
Bottom Right .... 125.00+

Page 85

Top (each) .... 10.00+
Bottom (each) .... 8.00+

Page 86

Top Picture
    #1, #3 (each) .... 15.00+
    #2, #4 (each) .... 10.00+
    #5 .... 15.00+

Bottom (each) .... 15.00+

Page 87

Top Picture
    #1, #2 ,#3 (each) .... 5.00+
    #4, #5, #6 (each) .... 10.00+
    #7 .... 6.00+
Bottom Picture
    #1, #3 (each) .... 10.00+
    #2 .... 15.00+
    #4 .... 35.00+

#5 .... 20.00+
#6 .... 25.00+

Page 88

Top Left Picture
    top left .... 5.00+
    top right .... 15.00+
    middle left .... 5.00+
    middle right................. 5.00+
    bottom .... 5.00+
Bottom Left .... 20.00+
Bottom Right Picture
    top .... 20.00+
    bottom .... 8.00+

Page 89

Top Left (each) .... 10.00+
Top Right Picture
    top .... 50.00+
    bottom .... 30.00+
Bottom Left .... 40.00+
Bottom Middle .... 40.00+
Bottom Right Picture
    top .... 65.00+
    bottom .... 100.00+

Page 90

Top Picture
    left .... 45.00+
    right .... 10.00+
Bottom Picture
    top .... 25.00+
    bottom left................. 25.00+
    bottom right .... 15.00+

Page 91

Top Picture
    #1 .... 20.00+
    #2 .... 40.00+
    #3 .... 15.00+
    #4 .... 35.00+
    #5 .... 30.00+
    #6 .... 40.00+
    #7 .... 100.00+
Bottom Picture
    #1, #3, #6, #7, #8(ea) .. 25.00+
    #2, #5 .... 20.00+
    #4 .... 100.00+
    #9 .... 35.00+

Page 92

Top Left Picture
    top .... 60.00+
    bottom .... 45.00+
Top Right Picture
    top .... 75.00+
    bottom .... 60.00+
Bottom Left 150.00-
Middle Right .... 65.00+
Bottom Right .... 125.00+

Page 93

Top Picture
    top left .... 15.00+
    top right .... 15.00+
    bottom .... 25.00+
Bottom (each) .... 20.00+

Page 94

Top Left .... 75.00+
Top Right .... 20.00+
Bottom .... 30.00+

Page 95

Top Left .... 75.00+
Top Right .... 40.00+
Middle Left .... 65.00+
Middle .... 35.00+
Middle Right .... 15.00+
Bottom Left .... 15.00+
Bottom Right .... 45.00+

Page 96

Top (each) .... 40.00+
Bottom Picture
   left .... 35.00+
   right .... 40.00+

Page 97

Top Left (each) .... 50.00+
Top Right .... 75.00+
Middle Right .... 50.00+
Bottom Left Picture
   left .... 60.00+
   right .... 75.00+

Page 98

Top Left (each) .... 60.00+
Top Right .... 50.00+
Bottom (each) .... 60.00+

Page 99

Top Left Picture
   top .... 25.00+
   middle .... 65.00+
   bottom .... 30.00+
Top Right Picture
   left .... 50.00+
   right .... 45.00+
Bottom Left .... 300.00+
Bottom Right (each) .... 50.00+

Page 100

Top Left (each) .... 100.00+
Top Right (each) .... 125.00+
Bottom Left Picture
   left .... 150.00+
   middle .... 250.00+
   right .... 75.00+
Bottom Right Picture
   top .... 150.00+
   bottom .... 200.00+

Page 101

Top (each) .... 50.00+
Middle .... 30.00+
BottomLeft .... 50.00+
Botttom Right .... 75.00+

Page 102

Top Left (each) .... 50.00+
Top Middle Picture

Page 103

top .... 60.00+
bottom .... 125.00+
Top Right (each) .... 100.00+
Bottom Left .... 40.00+
Bottom Right .... 50.00+

Page 103

Top Left Picture
   #1, #3 .... 25.00+
   #2 .... 35.00+
   #4 .... 30.00+
   #5, #6 .... 50.00+
Top Right (each) .... 50.00+
Bottom Left .... 30.00+
Bottom Middle .... 35.00+
Bottom Right .... 50.00+

Page 104

Top (each) .... 15.00-25.00+
Bottom (each) .... 15.00+

Page 105

Top Left .... 25.00+
Top Right Picture
   top .... 20.00+
   bottom .... 25.00+
Bottom Left .... 50.00+
Bottom Middle .... 125.00+
Bottom Right .... 7.00+

Page 106

Top (each) .... 25.00+
Bottom (each) .... 20.00+

Page 107

Top .... 75.00+
Bottom .... 35.00+

Page 108

Top Left .... 100.00+
Top Right .... 150.00+
Bottom Left .... 75.00+
Bottom Right .... 50.00+

Page 109

Top .... 350.00+
Bottom .... 350.00+

Page 110

Top .... 400.00+
Bottom Left .... 300.00+
Bottom Right .... 400.00+

Page 111

Top .... 175.00+
Bottom Left Picture
   top .... 200.00+
   bottom .... 150.00+
Bottom Middle .... 100.00+
Bottom Right .... 75.00+

Page 112

Top Picture
   top left .... 185.00+
   top right .... 140.00+

bottom .... 140.00+
Bottom Picture
   top .... 75.00+
   bottom .... 50.00+

Page 113

Top (each) .... 100.00+
Bottom (each) .... 150.00+

Page 114

Top Left Picture
   top .... 100.00+
   middle left .... 100.00+
   middle right .... 150.00+
   bottom left .... 175.00+
   bottom right .... 150.00+
Bottom (each) .... 150.00+

Page 115

Top Left (each) .... 125.00+
Top Right (each) .... 200.00+
Bottom Left .... 45.00+
Bottom Right Picture
   top .... 75.00+
   bottom .... 100.00+

Page 116

Top Left Picture
   top .... 300.00+
   left .... 150.00+
   bottom .... 100.00+
Bottom .... 300.00+

Page 117

Top Left Picture
   top .... 75.00+
   bottom .... 100.00+
Top Right Picture
   top .... 100.00+
   bottom .... 85.00+
Bottom .... 200.00+

Page 118

Top Left .... 90.00+
Top Right .... 40.00+
Bottom Left .... 75.00+
Bottom Middle .... 75.00+

Page 119

Top Left Picture
   top .... 100.00+
   bottom .... 200.00+
Top Right Picture
   left .... 65.00+
   right .... 50.00+
Bottom Left .... 85.00+
Bottom Middle .... 65.00+
Bottom Right .... 85.00+

Page 120

Top .... 125.00+
Bottom .... 65.00+

Page 121

Magazine Ad 3.00-5.00

Page 122

Magazine Ad 3.00-5.00

Page 123

Top Left .... 750.00+
Top Middle .... 60.00+
Top Right .... 75.00+
Bottom Left .... 135.00+
Bottom Middle .... 20.00+
Bottom Right .... 150.00+

Page 124

Top Left .... 75.00+
Top Right .... 25.00+
Middle .... 75.00+
Bottom Left .... 125.00+
Bottom Middle .... 50.00+
Bottom Right .... 30.00+

Page 125

Top .... 60.00+
Bottom Left .... 150.00+
Bottom Middle .... 50.00+
Bottom Right .... 100.00+

Page 126

All on page each .... 150.00+

Page 127

Top Left .... 75.00+
Top Right .... 35.00+
Middle Left (each) .... 20.00+
Bottom Left .... 3.00+
Bottom Right .... 30.00+

Page 128

Top Left Picture
    left .... 15.00+
    right .... 25.00+
Top Right .... 15.00+
Bottom Left .... 35.00+
Bottom Right (each) .... 10.00+

Page 129

Reference only

Page 130

Reference only

Page 131

Reference only

Page 132

No. 83J313 .... 75.00+
No. 83J314 .... 75.00+
No. 83J239 .... 100.00+
No. 83J45 .... 75.00+
No. 83J315 .... 75.00+
No. 83J316 .... 75.00+
No. 83J317 .... 100.00+
No. 83J318 .... 100.00+
No. 83J319 .... 100.00+
No. 83J358 .... 100.00+
No. 83J247 .... 325.00+

Page 133

No. 83J311 .... 50.00+
No. 83J312 .... 50.00+
No. 83J353 .... 50.00+
No. 83J354 .... 100.00+
No. 83J234 .... 175.00+
No. 83J43 .... 75.00+
No. 83J109 .... 100.00+
No. 83J44 .... 5.00+
No. 83J329 .... 15.00+

Page 134

No. 83J359 .... 300.00+
No. 83J197 .... 300.00+
No. 83J288 .... 450.00+
No. 83J289 .... 275.00+

Page 135

Top Row (each) .... 60.00+
Middle Row (each) .... 75.00+
Bottom Row (each) .... 85.00+

Page 136

All on page (each) .... 35.00+
    (if in excellent condition)

Page 137

No. 83J321 .... 150.00+
No. 83J322 .... 175.00+
No. 83J106 .... 150.00+
No. 83J236 .... 175.00+
No. 83J249 .... 325.00+
No. 83J330 .... 200.00+
No. 83J331 .... 250.00+
No. 83J196 .... 400.00+

Page 138

No. 83J328 .... 75.00+
No. 83J326 .... 100.00+
No. 83J245 .... 100.00+
No. 83J327 .... 100.00+
No. 83J112 .... 125.00+
No. 83J320 .... 75.00+
No. 83J242 .... 150.00+
No. 83J323 .... 75.00+
No. 83J324 .... 175.00+

Page 139

No. 83J361 .... 60.00+
Row 2 .... 50.00+
Row 3 .... 60.00+
Row 4 .... 60.00+
No. 83J194 .... 75.00+

Smoking Collectibles
A Price Guide

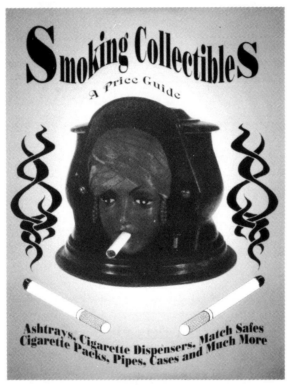

 # 1070

Some of the Hottest collectibles of recent years are smoking items and accessories. Spreading like wildfire, old advertising & tobacco paraphernalia are being swapped, shopped and sold throughout the country. L-W Books proudly presents Smoking Collectibles - A Price Guide to meet the needs of avid collectors everywhere. Get fired up and order your copy today - or you'll be fuming!!. 8 1/2" x 11", Color Photos, Paperback.

$14.95 + $2.00 Shipping for the first book 40¢ each additional

Send Check or Money order to:

L-W Book Sales

P.O. Box 69

Gas City, IN 46933

Or Call 1-800-777-6450 for Visa, Mastercard & C.O.D.

Orders Only!

Cigarette Lighter Price Guide

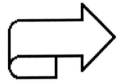

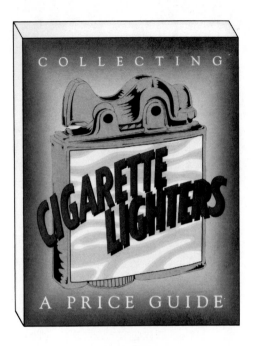

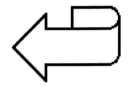

 # 1060

Light up your library with this very successful book. This volume has over 60 original catalog pages. Included are many original ads, black and white older photos and over 85 pages of living color (over 185 total pages). This book covers pocket, table, trench, electric, battery and store lighters. All lighters are illustrated or photographed and are priced. Already into its second printing GET YOUR ORDERS READY NOW!

$24.95+ $2.00 shipping

Add 40¢ shipping for each additional book.

Send Check or Money Order to:

L-W Book Sales, P.O. Box 69, Gas City, IN 46933

Or call

1-800-777-6450 for **Visa**, **Mastercard** and **C.O.D.** Orders Only!